John Peter Thomas

The Quest for the Holy Grail of Graig Trewyddfa, Swansea

An Illustrated Account of Mining
the Great Penvilian Black Diamonds 1717–1955

*1830 Gastineau-print of the White Rock and Hafod Copperworks
on the River Tawe, Swansea. Courtesy City and County of Swansea.
Swansea Museum Collection.*

novum ◢ pro

This book is also available as e-book.

www.novum-publishing.co.uk

© 2020 novum publishing

ISBN 978-3-99064-708-0
Editing: Ashleigh Brassfield
Cover photos: Courtesy British Library, Topographical Drawings;
Kurt Adams | Dreamstime.com
Cover design, layout & typesetting: novum publishing
Internal illustrations: see bibliography p.326

The images provided by the author have been printed in the highest possible quality.

www.novum-publishing.co.uk

Young girl pulling a cart of coal underground fitted with towing chain and girdle 1842. Commission of Enquiry into the State of Children in Employment in 1842

1870 View of the Port of Swansea showing the intense level of air pollution from the metal smelting industries in the lower Swansea Valley. Courtesy Swansea Docks Collection.

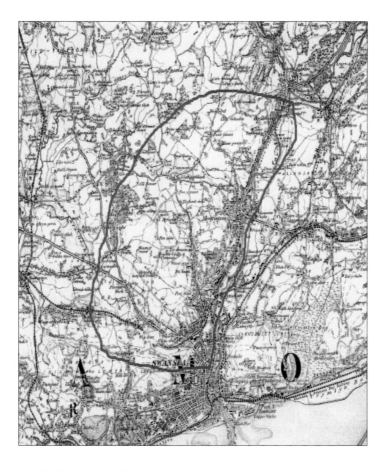

1870 O.S. Map of Lower Swansea Valley showing the area covered by this study. Courtesy O.H.M.S

CONTENTS

TO MY LATE PARENTS . . .
TOM and TILLY

THE AUTHOR

John 'Peter' Thomas, having spent his younger days living in the Swansea districts of St. Thomas, Sandfields, Garngoch, and Gowerton, moved to Morriston, the cradle of Britain's copper smelting industry, in the 1960s. What first struck him was the vast lunar landscape of copper slag heaps intertwined with derelict metal smelting works on the valley floor, stretching from Morriston to Landore and beyond. The whole area was devoid of vegetation due to the ground having been contaminated by copper smelting waste slag and former acid rain emissions. The following photographs highlight the scenes he witnessed:

Abandoned railway and waste copper slag tips near Morriston, Swansea Valley c. 1960s. Courtesy Swansea Docks Collection.

*The lunar landscape of copper slag boulders at Morriston.
April 1960. J.P.Thomas.*

*1960s View of the derelict White Rock Copperworks with the back
drop of mountains of toxic waste slag on Kilvey Hill.
Courtesy. D. Hague*

Copper slag tip almost at a resident's front door in Aberdyberthi Street, Hafod Swansea c. 1960. This tip was eventually cleared and Pentrehafod Comprehensive School was built on the reclaimed land. Hafod: Swansea Recalled.wordpress.com.

1961 Picture near Landore showing heaps of waste copper slag almost topping the nearby works. Courtesy R.W.Jones

The Legacy of Copper: The Landore/Hafod area in the 1920s as smelting was on the decline. Note the ramp (reminiscent of the one constructed by the Romans at Masada in the Judean Desert.) built by the Vivians to transport their Hafod Works' waste slag for dumping on Kilvey Hill. Courtesy COFLEIN.

Remains of Vivian's ramp built from the valley floor at Landore to Kilvey Hill to dispose waste toxic slag from the smelting works. The bridge carried the ramp over the Swansea Vale Railway. January 2018. J.P.Thomas

Coupled with this lunar landscape were the derelict coal mines, railways and tramroads surrounding Graig Trewyddfa at Morriston, Plasmarl, Brynhyfryd and Landore, which once supplied the copperworks with the bituminous coal needed to fire their smelting furnaces in the lower Swansea Valley during the eighteenth, nineteenth and twentieth centuries.

Much of the local coal mining history and its links with the copper smelting industry remains unaccounted for: without the local availability of the rich bituminous smokeless coal, smelting works would not have been established in the district in the first place, and neither the polluting toxic slag waste that followed. Moreover, the competition between local coal entrepreneurs to seek the best reserves of bituminous coal to sell to the metal smelting enterprises and the dire conditions the mining communities faced working in the depths of the earth to retrieve this commodity have received little attention. This inspired him to seek out these links, which together made Swansea the most polluted copper-smelting capital of the world.

He attended Dynevor Grammar School, Swansea, Swansea College of Technology, and later, the universities of Birmingham and Wales, where he graduated. He also served an engineering apprenticeship followed by several years experience in manufacturing and engineering and the local mining industry at the now closed Brynlliw Colliery, Grovesend. At the time of writing he is employed as a lecturer in Engineering and Design at Gower College, Gorseinon. He has a long-term interest in the industrial history of the Swansea district and has published a journal article entitled 'A Consideration of Technical Education in the Swansea District 1800–1900', which appeared in the International Journal 'Vocational Aspects of Education' in 1979. More recently he published a book entitled 'The Rise and Fall of the Penclawdd Canal and Railway or Tramroad Company 1811–1865.

PREFACE

The general view of writers investigating Swansea's metallurgical industries is that with the growth of copper smelting in the lower Swansea valley in the eighteenth century, local attitudes towards copper smelting showed that many accepted that copper smoke was an inconvenience that had to be tolerated if it could not be practically or economically remedied. Certainly, many who suffered the effects of copper smoke owed their livelihood directly or indirectly to the copper industry and were prepared to accept its less attractive aspects. Indeed, "copper smoke", a cocktail of noxious vapors and particles given off by ores when smelted mixed with coal smoke from furnace fuel, was acknowledged as one of the most potent forms of industrial pollution in Britain.

View of the copper smelting Industries
on the river Tawe at Landore C 1850.

This sentiment is expressed in the lyrics of the "Song of the Copper Smoke," which appeared in the 1871 'Tourist's Companion in Swansea' and includes the lines:

> "I touch the tall trees with my vapoury hand,
> And their leaves drop off, like courtiers bland...
> You may search the vale and the mountain high
> There is not a flower to gladden the eye."

But it ends with the verse:

> "The widow's lone bosom I thrill with joy,
> As I fill the hands of her orphan boy,
> The miner I help in the sunless cave;
> By me rich merchants their fortunes save;
> Barristers, bankers, and even clod-hoppers
> Would feel very small if they hadn't 'some coppers'."

Those who perhaps suffered the most personal discomfort from copper smoke were employees of copper works and others living in industrial communities near the works, such as Morriston and Vivian Town [Hafod/Landore], but there are no reports to suggest that copper smoke was ever the subject of industrial action on their part. In law, private nuisance refers to the unreasonable interference with another's use or enjoyment of his or her land, and public nuisance is that which obstructs or causes inconvenience or discomfort to the public. Awareness of potential legal action over nuisance and the early intervention of the local corporation to zone industry ensured that smelting works in Swansea were located on the eastern edge of the town, so that the prevailing westerly winds blew the smoke across wasteland. However, Thomas Williams' 1854 report on the Copper Smoke claimed the northerly and northwesterly winds frequently brought smoke across the town, and places farther up the Swansea Valley, such as Llansamlet and Morriston, were often affected. If the wind was in the right direction, inhabitants could be forced to breathe in fumes which caused a bitter metallic taste in the mouth, a dry sensation in the throat, loss of appetite, frayed tempers, a tight feeling across the chest, and watering and smarting of the eyes.

The most striking feature of copper smoke, however, was its impact on vegetation. The following description, written by Daniel Webb in 1812, whilst travelling in south Wales, is typical of those made by travellers who passed by smelting sites: "... about a mile or two towards the entrance of Swansea, the appearance is frightful, the smoke of the copper furnaces having entirely destroyed the herbage; and the vast banks of scoriae surrounding the works, together with the volumes of smoke arising from the numerous fires, gives the country a volcanic appearance."

At greater distances from copper works the concentration of smoke was diluted and the damage less severe, but the effects of acid rain and dry deposition of pollutants were still noticeable. It was claimed by Daniel Webb that animals grazing within a radius of several miles of certain works suffered poisoning from arsenic, and there were frequent complaints about "smoke disease", or "efrydd-dod", the symptoms of which were swollen joints and rotting teeth, which would eventually kill the animals unless they were removed to better pasture.

Moreover, the Cambrian of 6 August 1858 reported that the damp atmosphere and high levels of rainfall made acid rain a problem in the towns, as could be seen from its effects on stone and paintwork and the discoloration and corrosion of windows. Its effect on vegetation could be devastating and almost instantaneous. As one farmer complained, "it shrivels up the grass and the straw almost as gone over it."

Land in close proximity to the copper works affected by both acid rain and the dry deposition of pollutants, such as the western side of Kilvey Hill in Swansea, was often completely denuded.

Confusion about the potential health problems associated with copper smoke tended to complicate potential law suits against smelting firms. In 1842, a Royal Commission report claimed that smelter smoke had kept Swansea free from the cholera epedemics in the early 1830s. Indeed there may be some truth in this claim, as a witness, Morag Leune, suggested the sulphur and arsenic-laced smoke may have served as a chemical fumigant and disinfectant. Furthermore, a bath in the sulfurous "yellow scum covered quenching water" from the first fusion of the Welsh smelting process was once said to cure mange in dogs.

In an attempt to reduce the threat of legal action, and perhaps more importantly, to benefit economically from the recovery of by-products that otherwise quite literally went up in smoke, smelting firms including the Vivian and Sons' Hafod works and Williams, Foster & Co's Morfa works, employed eminent scientists like Michael Faraday and Richard Phillips to advise as to the best means of dealing with the problem. The earliest and most widely used technology involved using the Geerstenhofer furnace and constructing tall chimney stacks to which all or most of the furnaces at a copper works were connected by long flues. Some of the arsenic, sulphur, and hydrochloric acid would condense in the flues and the stacks as the smoke cooled, and that which passed out of the stacks was dispersed more widely; materials collected in the flues could be used to produce by-products such as arsenic and sulphuric acid.

When Henry Hussey Vivian was elevated to the peerage as the First Lord of Swansea in 1893, it was claimed over-enthusiastically that one of his major achievements was to transform "poisonous copper smoke into a useful by-product."

The purpose in writing this account is not to examine the pollution caused by the copper works in the lower Swansea Valley, which is well documented, but to focus attention on the demands placed by the hungry copper smelters on the coal owners and local mining communities situated in the lower Swansea valley, who were employed in the bowels of the earth to cut out the coal to feed them. There were no mechanised coal cutting machinery at this time. Colliers and their families, including children, worked in dark, dismal, cold, cramped, damp, and dangerous conditions using basic hand cutting tools. Where the coal seams were narrow, child labour was usually employed to drag the cut coal in carts or tubs from the face to the mine entrance or pit bottom, for transportation. Moreover, pockets of methane (fire damp) gas lurked at the coal face, awaiting ignition by a spark from the clashing of steel tools or by open candlelight. As we shall see, urban pollution, loss of life, and injury in the name of copper production was inevitable.

Indeed, it was the mining communities, which supplied the bituminous coal necessary to charge the smelting furnaces, which eventually led to Swansea becoming the world centre for copper smelting and aptly named 'Copperopolis'. I make no apology for the frequent number of quotations in this work. Most are descriptive, and some refer to the work of other writers.

The story that will unfold is complicated, primarily because so intensively was the area mined, and for so long, it is difficult to establish an exact diary of the various undertakings and, in some cases, to differentiate from one undertaking to another. However, most of the mining activities discussed relate to Graig Trewyddfa, in the Swansea district of south Wales.

I especially wish to record my sincere thanks and appreciation to the staff of numerous organisations and libraries who have assisted me in the various stages of my research either by conversation or correspondence, especially the following: Mike Wildin, local coal industry historian; Ian Neville, for his assistance in setting out the manuscript; my son, Julian, and granddaughter, Jade, for archiving the numerous photographs and illustrations; Swansea Reference Library; Swansea Museum Library; West Glamorgan Archives; Glamorgan Archives; Swansea University Library Richard Burton Archives; National Library of Wales; Royal Commission for Ancient Monuments in Wales; South Wales Miner's Library; Fforestfach Historical Society; the Morriston History Group; the Rev. Ian Rees, for allowing us entry to St. John's Church, Hafod; and particularly the works of Joanna Martin, Paul Reynolds, Gerald Gabb, Norman Thomas, Treboeth Historical Society and the Welsh Coal Mines Forum on the district's coal mining industry, which provided useful research platforms.

It is also hoped that the chapter surrounding the 'Myth of the Clyndu Navigational Canal' in the Clyndu Level Colliery, in Morriston, will prove to be of added interest to readers.

JOHN PETER THOMAS

INTRODUCTION

The growth of Swansea as an industrial centre is believed to have commenced around 1717, on the initiative of Gabriel Powell. In his post as steward to the Duke of Beaufort he advocated that the copper industry be started in Swansea, pointing out its accessibility and proximity to the ports in Cornwall where copper ore was obtainable, local sources of cheap and suitable coal, and the harbour for transport.

The Industrial Revolution in south Wales brought about a tremendous change in the production of copper and its alloys. An insistent demand arose for more and higher quality raw material. In 1586 Ulrich Fosse, a German who was working the Cumberland copper mines, boasted that he could smelt 560 tons of copper ore in forty weeks. The 17th and 18th centuries saw a vast improvement in this rate of output, largely arising from a faster removal of impurities from the ore during the calcining process. By 1717 the Landore Works at Swansea comprised three large buildings, one of which was devoted solely to calcining. There were also thirty smelting furnaces for copper, lead, and silver, a refining house, a test house, and other outbuildings.

Moreover, by 1794 the nearby Mines Royal at Neath Abbey were smelting 230 tons of copper ore per week to give 18 tons of copper. They used 38 furnaces, which consumed 315 tons of coal in the operation. The presence and availability of good quality coal, in fact, was one of the reasons why the Swansea district became the centre of this industry; charcoal had been used right down to 1688, although as early as 1632 Edward Jorden discovered a new method of smelting by using pit coal, peat and turf as a fuel, and four years later Sir Philip Vernatt was granted a patent for the use of coal alone for that purpose.

These developments led to the eventual use of coal as the primary fuel for the smelting of copper.[1]

During the 18th century, production in the nearby Cornish mines increased, and a high output was sustained due to the introduction of steam pumps to remove the water from the diggings. This was the first use of steam power in mining, and arose from the inventive mind of Thomas Newcomen, a Dartmouth blacksmith.

Clearly, the advantages of establishing copper smelting enterprises in Swansea were its unrivalled access to sutable coal and limestone in the Glamorgan coalfield and access to the sea at Swansea, with tidal waters up to many of the locations of smelters. It was the closest location to the copper ore mines of Cornwall, although this could never be considered an easy passage for the small sailing vessels used in the shipment of coal and ore to and from Cornwall.[2] These advantages led to Swansea becoming the greatest centre in the world of copper smelting and refining, a distinction which it retained until the latter part of the 19th Century.

Moreover, it was generally argued that the cost of shipping coal to Cornwall was the main reason for it being uncompetitive to smelt copper ore at its source in Cornwall. In the 1730s it was estimated that the production one ton of copper required 10 tons of ore and five and one half weys of coal, that is, approximately 30 tons.[3] Thus transport costs would appear to be three times greater to smelt ore in Cornwall.

An indication of the growth in traffic is given by the number of vessels using the Port of Swansea:

Year	1768	1790	1791	1792	1793
Vessels	694	1,697	1,803	1,828	2,028

This represented a near threefold increase in 25 years, of which perhaps half would be in the copper ore and coal trades. Over the same period the tonnage increased from 631 tons to 120,828 tons, an increase of the order of 52%in the size of the vessels using the port.[4]

The growth of copper smelting in Swansea led to greater demands for ore, firstly from Cornwall, then Parys in Anglesey, and finally the wider world of South America, to feed the hungry furnaces of the lower Swansea valley works. But a terrible price was to be paid; the local atmosphere in what had formerly been the beautiful green Tawe valley became so foul with sulfurous fumes that it was said by local inhabitants that if the Devil were to pass that way he would think he was going home.[5]

It follows that copper enterprises began to seek a regular and suitable supply of clean smokeless fuel capable of producing the most intensive heat in smelting furnaces. Their 'holy grail' lay buried in the Great Penvilian Five Foot Coal Vein of Graig Trewyddfa, which covered an area stretching from Cwm Clydach to Cwm Burlais, covering Llangyfelach, Morriston, Plasmarl, Landore, Brynhyfryd, Treboeth, and Cwm Burlais; and so local mine owners and copper smelters began their quest to seek out the lucrative 'black diamonds'. This search, according to some writers, necessitated the construction of an underground navigational canal at the Clyndu colliery, Morriston, to ship coal from the mine to the Forest Copperworks.

INTRODUCTION.
BIBLIOGRAPHY AND ILLUSTRATIONS

(1) W.O. Alexander. Development of the Copper, Zinc and Brass Industries of Great Britain from AD 1500–1900. Murex Rev, 1955. P.399
(2) Letter Box of the Tin Contract. Truro. 1703–10. Cornish Record Office.

(3) Caution must be observed in the conversion of volume to tons: it varied from port to port.

(4) Universal British Directory Vol. 4 (1791) p.520.

(5) W.O.Alexander, 1955, p.408.

Mining Terminology used in this study

LEVEL – a mine roadway which is more or less horizontal. It can be an entry from the ground surface, i.e. perhaps driven into a hillside, or else be completely underground. They could be either in-seam or cross-measure. Levels which were driven in-seam will, by definition, follow the strike or level-course of the seam, a direction at right-angles to the direction of full dip (maximum gradient) of the seam. Levels were often used as water-drainage roadways and In this case they would normally have a slight gradient (1 in 100 to 1 in 300) to allow the water to flow out steadily. Less than that, the water would not flow freely and be prone to silting up; if steeper than that, the increased water velocity would tend to erode gullies in the roadway floor.

SLANT – a term used in South Wales to describe an inclined mine entry from the surface to a target seam. This usually means that it is a cross-measure drift from the surface, but can also refer to an adit driven in-seam in dipping strata.

ADIT – a walkable mine entry, driven in-seam from the surface outcrop position of the seam, often into the side of a hill (in the South Wales valleys), following the seam, therefore at the same dip (gradient) of the seam. Sometimes synonymous with 'drift' but the latter, strictly speaking, implies a mine entry or mine roadway which cuts across the strata.

PIT – an individual shaft

COLLIERY – an entire coal mining operation, including all infrastructures from offices to transport, and may include several pits (shafts) or drifts.

DRIFT – a drift mine is an underground mine in which the entry or access is above water level and generally on the slope of a hill, driven horizontally into the ore seam. Drift is a more general mining term, meaning a near-horizontal passageway in a mine, following the bed (of coal, for instance) or vein of ore.

SYNCLINE – is a steep valley underground, as opposed to ANTICLINE – a hill.

TRAMROAD and TRAMWAY mean the same thing.

RAILROAD – is the name given to a tramroad laid to the standard railway gauge of 4' 8½ inches enabling its coal trucks to carry heavier loads and interchange with the local railway network.

CHAPTER I

THE SEARCH FOR 'BLACK DIAMONDS' ON THE TURBULENT COMMONS SURROUNDING GRAIG TREWYDDFA

The smelting of metal ores is a very old technology and has always used large quantities of fuel. The metal smelting industries grew through their use of charcoal, a major contributor to the destruction of woodland in Britain and elsewhere. The shift to coal caused by the scarcity, and hence rising price, of charcoal in the 18th Century led to smelters being located close to coal mines rather than metal [ore] mines. This was because the process of smelting copper took 70–100 hours and 13–18 tons of coal costing 5 shillings per ton were required to make one ton of copper being consumed in the first and second operations of roasting and melting. [1] Progessive simplifications to the copper smelting process, including the development of the reverberatory furnace, substantially reduced fuel use, and by the early 1900s typical fuel use was one ton of coal per ton of copper.[2] But it was rarely the case that the consumer, and also the source of ore, would be found in proximity with the requisite amounts of fuel. With these three factors being decentralised an efficient transport system became essential. Throughout the eighteenth century the most cost effective means for the bulk transport of commodities like coal and copper ore was carriage by sea or canal, a further constraint on the location of an economically efficient smelter. Between the mines and the ports conveyance was on the backs of horses and mules.[3]

The use of coal for copper smelting was certainly one justification for the concentration of copperworks in South Wales. Hence very large quantities of copper ores and regulus were brought to Swansea (where a reliable supply of bituminous smelting coal was available) to be smelted, from Chile, from the Cape, from Portugal and elsewhere, because it cost less to bring the ore to the coal than to send the coal to the ore. [4]

It was during the period of the development of mining and copper smelting in eighteenth century south Wales that the local gentry found the profits from the exploitation of the mineral resources of their estates a welcome addition to an agricultural income limited by the generally poor land of the area, including Cwm Burlais, Treboeth/Landore, Plasmarl, and Morriston, situated in and around Graig Trewyddfa in the Seignory of Gower; land which had hitherto been fit only for the grazing of sheep. This land thus acquired a new importance and disputes over the ownership of particular pieces of ground which in which nobody had previously shown any great interest were frequent and sometimes bitter.[5]

Freeholders held the rights to the minerals under their own land, but the Duke of Beaufort claimed the minerals under the commons and copyhold lands in the Seignory of Gower, and this applied to much of the land covering the coalfield. Disputes therefore arose as to the boundaries of tenements, whether particular pieces of land were freehold or copyhold, and how far the commons extended. The growth of both the mining and copper smelting industries led to an increasing demand for wood for pit props and coal suitable for metal smelting. This resulted in small patches of poor woodland, and land bearing coal reserves, being hotly contested.[6]

The 'Holy Grail' which lay beneath the lands of Graig Trewyddfa, locally known as the 'Great Penvilia Five Foot Vein', was renowned for its qualities and demand for the domestic market, steam generating boilers and smelting furnaces:

"This coal has a fine fibrous structure, a shining black colour, is compact, but may be broken without difficulty into suitable lumps for burning. It kindles readily, burns with a bright, white, copious flame, *but without smoke,* capable of affording a powerfully diffusive heat to the flues of steam and other boilers. … it affords no gaseous excess to cause the production of smoke, as the Newcastle and other rich bituminous Coals do. It is in this respect intermediate between bituminous and anthracite Coal, and is preferably greatly to both for generating steam.

One hundred parts afford 81 ¼ of silvery-looking coke, capable of producing a most intensive heat in smelting furnaces."[7]

The unique qualities of this smokeless coal, which produced intensive heat in smelting furnaces, made it Graig Trewyddfa's 'holy grail' because of the demand for its high value benefits to the developing copper smelting industries in the lower Swansea valley. What followed was a localised 'Klondike', with a rush to discover and open up the lucrative bituminous coal seams, which were close to the surface, for extraction and profit.

The South Wales Directory of 1835 reported, "The smelting of copper ore is carried on here to the amount of about one hundred and twenty thousand tons annually, and it takes about two tons of coal to smelt one ton of copper. Some idea may be formed of the immense consumption of the former in the neighbourhood of Swansea. The mines of bituminous and stone coal [anthracite]and culm are very numerous and prolific throughout the whole district; limestone is also found in great abundance; and brick and fire clay, rotten stone, iron ore and other mineral productions are met with."[8]

The Duke of Beaufort's Agents, Stewards and Bailiffs during this period were Gabriel Powell Senior, and his son, also named Gabriel, who succeeded in making himself one of the most unpopular men in Glamorgan during his fifty-year tenure of the stewardship.[9]

Gabriel Senior, who resided at Heathfield Lodge, Swansea, died on 13 November 1813: he was known as Captain Sir Gabriel Powell, J.P., Captain of the Fairwood Troop of Yeomantry which he formed in 1778. He was also a Swansea Corporation Trustee, Alderman, and Deputy Steward to the Duke of Beaufort for the Seignory of Gower.

(Plate 1) Henry Somerset, Sixth Duke of Beaufort.
Courtesy National Portrait Gallery

Neither Gabriel Powell Senior, nor his son, were slow to recognise the probable benefits to the Duke of Beaufort of the opening-up of the industrial resources of the area. In the words of Gabriel Powell Junior, "The coal under the commons of Llangyfelach and Llandeilo-talybont are of very great value and will one day or other produce many thousand pounds"[10] In addition to royalties for coal mined under the Duke's land, revenue came from land leased for copperworks and for cottages for the copper workers and colliers and the granting of permission to build wharves and weirs on the Tawe, and from sales of timber.[11]

The rivers and streams of the area, of which the ownership was likewise often uncertain, also assumed a new importance. Due to the appalling state of the region's roads, any bulky goods, such as coal, timber, copper and iron, were transported by water wherever possible; in addition to this, water-power was a vital source of energy. Thus, all the early copper works in the Swansea area – at Ynys-penllwch, Fforest, Landore and the White Rock – were sited on the banks of the Tawe.[12]

In 1717 Dr. John Lane of Bristol and John Pollard, both of whom had interest in Cornish Mining, moved from Neath Abbey to Llangyfelach in the parish of Landore to take advantage of the improved access to the sea and coal. There they remained until 1726, when the works were taken over by Morris Lockwood & Co.

Morris Lockwood & Co. continued at Llangyfelach until 1748, but increased their facilities by building a new smelter, the Cambrian Works, in 1720. This they occupied until 1745; following its disposal it was converted into a porcelain factory. In 1748 Morris and Lockwood moved northward up the river Tawe, establishing a new smelter at Upper Fforest, and the adjacent industrial village of Morristown. This they occupied until 1790, when they sold the works to the Bristol firm Harfords & Bristol Brass and Copper Company. Harfords remained there until no later than 1833, at which date the company ceased to be a copper and brass manufacturer. Lockwoods continued to operate the Landore facility until the early nineteenth century. By 1810, they had ceased submitting to the copper ticketing exchange in Cornwall.

However, troubles began to rumble in the 1720s with the arrival on the scene of Robert Morris, the first of the Morris family of Clasemont (the founders of Morriston) and one of the most prominent men in the early industrial history of the area.

Predictably, the Popkins of Fforest were foremost in the conflict, and disputes between the two families were to last until well into the nineteenth century. Robert Morris, whose family came from Cleobury Mortimer and Bishop's Castle (Salop), first became involved in the industrial development of Glamorgan c.1724 through his association with Dr. John Lane of Bristol, who in 1717 had taken from Thomas Popkins a lease of the old Llangyfelach Copperworks at Landore, near Swansea. In November 1726 Lane went bankrupt, largely, it would appear, as a result of unwise investment speculation. In the following year Morris, in partnership with Richard Lockwood, Edward Gibbon and Robert Corker, took over the Llangyfelach copper works.[13]

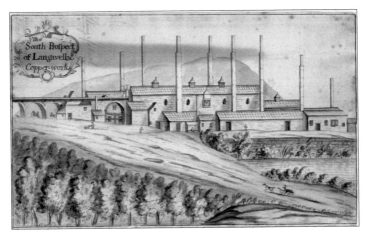

(Plate 2) View of the Llangyfelach Copper Works. Landore. SS 662958. C.1716. Courtesy British Library (Topographical Drawings)

The works were extensive and had 20 furnaces for smelting, a refinery house, a forge, a laboratory as well as a blast house and an accounting house. Located on the River Tawe, the factory was well situated for access to the port in Swansea, and because a coal mine already existed there. The refinery machinery was driven by a large overshot waterwheel which had a constant flow of water supplied from the Nant Rhyd-y-Filais and Nant-y-Cwm-Gelli crossing over a stone arched viaduct leading into the manufacturing facility.

Both the Popkins family and the Prices from Penllegaer had been among the worse culprits with regard to the illicit enclosure of the commons surrounding Graig Trewyddfa. Popkins had also erected a bridge across the Tawe without permission and demanded that those who crossed it should pay him a toll.[14]

Problems arose almost immediately, because Thomas Popkins, who had covenanted, in the original lease, to supply the copper works with coal at a reduced rate, was either unable or unwilling to fulfil his contract. It appears that he wished to sell his coal elsewhere at a higher price, and he supplied the copper works only with poor quality culm, which they could not use. Robert Morris needed 90 barrow loads of coal a day for his copper production, so he had to look elsewhere for coal – and at a less favourable price – and when the company tried to oblige Popkins to make up the difference, disputes were inevitable.[15]

At the time coal was carried in panniers from the coalworks to the river or copperworks by horses, and it was customary for the landlords of the area to insert in their leases a clause obliging tenants to provide one or more horses for this work. Morris suffered because he had little land and therefore few tenants of his own, whilst Popkins, who owned much of the land in the area, made sure that his own tenants would not carry coal for his rival. Morris could, therefore, only procure carriers by paying one shilling per wey more than the neighbouring coal proprietors.[16]

However, the increasing use of wagon-ways and tramways to carry goods brought more problems, for their construction often involved the crossing of land belonging to several different people and hence provided the occasion for further disputes.

Since a ready supply of coal for the copper works was essential, the next obvious step for Morris to take was the acquisition of at least a share in a neighbouring coalworks. This he achieved in August 1728, when he entered into an agreement with Kingsmill Mackworth, whose father, the famous (or rather infamous) Sir Humphrey Mackworth, had originally taken a lease of mines at Treboeth from the Somerset family in 1708. His son Kingsmill does not seem to have shared his father's enthusiasm for industrial enterprises and was described by Morris as ,but an indifferent collier'. Under the agreement, Robert Morris was to pay for the sinking of a new pit and then receive half the profits of the coalworks.[17]

In the following year (1729), Morris took from the Duke of Beaufort a lease of the Lower Fforest estate, which adjoined Popkins' freehold land and which the latter also apparently ,had an eye to'. His failure to obtain it only increased Popkins's animosity toward Morris and he succeeded in frustrating plans to build a new copper works there by refusing to allow his adversary permission to build a weir, one end of which had to be tied to Popkins' land. Nor was this the end of Thomas Popkins's attempts to impede the development of Morris' industrial concerns.[18]

At the same time, Morris received a general lease for ninety-nine years of veins of coal and culm under most of the Duke's lands in Gower, including the commons of Treboeth, Knap Llwyd, Mynydd Cam Llwyd, Trewyddfa, Forest, Blackpill Burrows and Sands, Swansea, Townhill and Gorseinon. This lease virtually gave Morris the right to mine coal anywhere he wished, except on land held by freeholders and, for the time being, under Thomas Price's customary land at Trewyddfa, for Price himself already had a grant of the mineral rights there. Much of the land in this part of Gower was held by copy of the court roll, a form of tenure which had over the years become virtually indistinguishable from freehold because the rents were fixed. But there was one exception: the Duke retained the mineral rights.[19]

The mid-1740s saw the beginning of a new and even more bitter stage in the Popkins-Morris dispute, along with attacks on Gabriel Powell and the Somerset family which threatened to undermine the latter's whole position in Gower. The event which precipitated these developments was the grant by the Duke to Morris, Lockwood and Co. of land at Upper Forest, situated a few miles up the Tawe from their Landore works, with liberty to build a new copper works there.[20]

Certainly, the Price family of Penllegaer, who had been mining coal since the 1660s, did not hesitate to use intimidation when it suited them. Some ten years earlier, Thomas Price's son, Griffith, had refused to sell coal to one David Phillip of Swansea, one of the town's sergeants-at-mace, because he had been employed by Gabriel Powell to break down the hedges of an encroachment – adjoining which Thomas Price had recently, and coincidentally, purchased a piece of land. Griffith Price was reported to have told Phillip, "Go about your business, you shall have no coal here", and he had, moreover, threatened to turn anyone who sold coal to him out of his coalworks.[21]

Hitherto, this had been an insignificant detail, for the Duke's agent had granted licences to mine coal on request in return for a nominal payment. Now, however, the copyholders – which included the Popkins family and the Prices – had reason to fear, not only that they would not be granted permission to mine coal under lands which they considered to be their own, but also that the coal would in fact be mined by someone else, over whom they had no control but who had the Duke's full support. Therefore, in addition to continuing attacks on Morris, Price and Popkins also began to question the Duke's right to make such a grant.[22]

So began a phase of attacks on Morris' coalworks in which Price and Popkins were joined by other neighbouring coal owners. In February 1748 it was reported by Morris to the Duke that a "Mr. John Jeffreys said he would join Mr. Price with all Mr. Powell's colliers to destroy [Morris'] level and [if] Mr. Gabriel Powell would not inter-meddle, they would soon demolish me and our works in general".[23] Price was also accused of threatening Morris' workmen, and himself accused Morris of "giving private orders to his Copper men to rise in case of any other obstruction given his workmen".[24] The latter accusation appears to have been entirely without foundation. During this period, too, one of Morris' collieries was set on fire, and Mr. Popkins built a wall across a coal level and drowned it, and Mr. Price at a great expense contrived to deprive another coalworks of air, by which six poor men were suffocated one evening.[25] This tragedy in discussed in greater detail in Chapter II.

On the morning of 29 November 1747 Thomas Price went with ,about twenty' workmen to a place near a lane called Heol Griffith, where Robert Morris' men were in the process of digging "a new level for the better draining of a considerable tract of land, where a large quantity of coal might be found". On arriving at the place concerned, "The said Thomas Price laid hold of the windlass and broke it down and then ordered David Thomas, one of his attendants, to go into the level and strike down the timbers which supported the earth." Price, whose objection was allegedly that Morris had no right to mine coal under the road (and in this he may well have been correct) was later reported to have said of Morris' workmen, "I will send them to gaol and they shall rot there."[26]

In the autumn of 1752, Gabriel Powell gave one of the Duke's tenants living near Gorseinon permission to cut wood in order to build a 'beasthouse'. Price tried to obstruct him and claimed that the wood belonged to him, since it had been cut down on his land — land which, Gabriel Powell said, was the lord's common. Powell then proceeded to cut down two of the trees to establish the Duke's right to them, whereupon someone — in other words, Price — had about twenty-one further trees felled.[27]

It was during these turbulent times in 1747, when the commons around Graig Trewyddfa must have resembled the 'Wild West', that the copper-smelting firm of Lockwood, Morris and Co., moved from their Llangyfelach works at Landore to the new site at Forest (Morriston). Here they established the Forest Copperworks, and production began in 1749, when the old works at Landore closed.

(Plate 3) 1761 View of Fforest Copper Works, Swansea along-side Beaufort Bridge, SS 669970. Published by Thomas Rothwell. Courtesy Swansea Museum Ceramics Section.

The architect for the new works was William Edwards. There were four unusual circular 'pavilions', each containing four reverbatory calcining furnaces, arranged' around a central octagonal refinery. The illustration above shows part of the works and the Beaufort Bridge, also designed by William Edwards. Out of the picture, on the opposite bank of the river Tawe was the Lower Forest copper rolling and battery mill designed by John Padmore, a water-power engineer from Bristol.

In 1746, Robert Morris greatly extended his coal interests by applying for a lease from the Duke of Beaufort that allowed him to work coal virtually anywhere on the western side of the Tawe between Landore and Morriston. He followed this by opening up the Five Foot Penvilia Vein around Craig Trewyddfa at Clyndu Level Colliery, Morriston, partly to supply his Forest works and partly to increase his exports of coal. His collieries were not far from the sea and he was keen to find a market for coals that might not be suitable for his furnaces. Moreover, the new works was situated at the 'Highest Point of the Ordinary Tide', which allowed vessels carrying copper ore to sail up the river Tawe and unload their cargoes directly at the copperworks.

By the late 1760s, conditions in the Gower seignory seem to have become quieter. Three of the main antagonists were dead: Thomas Popkins died c. 1751–52, Thomas Price in 1763 and Robert Morris in 1768. However, a legacy of bitterness and a determination to withstand any attempts, real or imagined, to extend the Duke's powers remained for some years to come.[28]

(Plate 4) Sir John Morris 1ˢᵗ Baronet.
Courtesy Rhys Owain Williams.

It is worth noting that following Robert Morris's death, his second son, **Sir John Morris** (1745–1819), expanded the family's copper-smelting and coal-mining interests in the Tawe valley throughout the remainder of the eighteenth century. John Morris also initiated in 1768 the building of the planned village of Morris Town (Morriston) in the northern part of Swansea, including 'Morris Castle', to house the company's workers, including a shoemaker and a tailor for their service.

The next chapter is devoted to the death of six colliers employed at the Clyndu Level Colliery by oxygen deprivation and the subsequent inquest.

CHAPTER I
BIBLIOGRAPHY AND ILLUSTRATIONS

(1) D. Percy, Cost and Consumption of Coal [in copper smelting] The Edinburgh Review, Vol 137, 1873, p.459 (2) P.F. (2) Chapman. F. Roberts, Metal Reserves and Energy, 1983, p.89, Butterworth & Co.

(3) J.C. Symons, The mining and Smelting of Copper in England and Wales 1760–1820, Unpublished Thesis, Coventry University. 2003

(4) P.F. Chapman. F. Roberts, p.89

(5) Joanna Martin 'Private Enterprise versus Manorial rights: mineral property disputes in Eighteenth Century Glamorgan. Welsh History Review Vol. 9, 1978–79. pp. 158–159 National Library of Wales.

(6) Ibid

(7) N. Cameron Prospectus. Proposed Swansea to Loughor Railway 1851.

(8) Pigot & Co. South Wales Directory 1835, P.789

(9) W.C. Rogers, Swansea and Glamorganshire Calendar, part1,Vol.II./ (Unpublished M.S. N.L.W.) quoted by Joanna Martin, Welsh History Review Vol. 9, 1978–79. P.158,

(10) N.L.W. Badmington MSS 2334

(11) Ibid.

(12) Joanna Martin P.161

(13) Ibid.p.164

(14) Ibid.p.162

(15) Ibid.p.163

(16) Ibid.p.162

(17) Ibid p.160

(18) Ibid p.165

(19) Ibid.

(20) N.L.W. Badmington MSS 19215

(21) Joanna Martin.P. 166na

(22) N.L.W. Badmington MSS 1491

(23) Ibid 1910

(24) Ibid 1931 (This tragedy is discussed in greater detail in
    Chapter II)

(25) N.L.W. Badmington MSS 1480

(26) Ibid. 1524

(27) Joanna Martin. P.172

(28) Ibid. p.174

(Plate 1) Portrait, Henry Somerset, Sixth Duke of Beaufort.
    Courtesy National Portrait Gallery

(Plate 2) View of the Llangyfelach Copper Works. Landore.
    C 1716.

(Plate 3) 1761 View of Forest Copper Works, Swansea along-
    side Beaufort Bridge, SS 669970. Published by Thomas
    Rothwell. Courtesy Swansea Museum Ceramics Section.

(Plate 4) Portrait, Sir John Morris 1st Baronet Courtesy Rhys
    Owain Williams

CHAPTER II

THE DEATH OF SIX COLLIERS EMPLOYED AT THE CLYNDU LEVEL MINE

It was during this phase of attacks on Morris' coalworks, in which Price and Popkins were joined by other neighbouring coal owners, that a tragic accident occurred at the Clyndu Level mine on 10th October, 1754. This was one of the first levels where the 'black gold' from the Penvilia Vein was being extracted on a large scale by John Morris. In an attempt to stall production, the workmen of a competitive mine owner, Thomas Price, blocked the air holes (ventilation shafts) of the level, which resulted in the deaths of six miners through carbonic poisoning. What follows is the full Coroner's report of the accident and deaths:[1]

The colliers who died through suffocation (by carbonic acid gas) were:

- John Walton of Trewyddfa – Inquisition held in his dwelling house in Trewyddfa
- Hopkin Phillips of Trewyddfa – Inquisition held in his dwelling house in Trewyddfa
- Griffith Lewis of Trewyddfa – Inquisition held in his dwelling house in Trewyddfa
- Mark Gray of Clyndu – Inquisition held in his dwelling house in Clyndu
- David Davies Abraham of Clyndu – Inquisition held in Mark Gray's dwelling house in Clyndu
- Thomas Rees of Twr Ych Fawr – Inquisition held in his dwelling house in Tyr Ych Fawr.

The Coroner's 'hand-written' reports for each victim follow the same composition (the grammar has not been changed) and the following Coroner's Report is that of 'Hopkin Phillips' who resided at Trewyddfa, Morriston.[2]

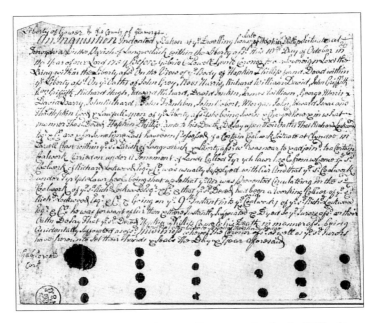

(Plate 1) Coroner's Handwritten Report on the death of 'Hopkin Phillip 'who resided at Trewyddfa, Morriston. 10 October 1754. National Library of Wales. Badmington Papers II

The grammar has not been changed in the following transcript:

"An Inquisition Indented and Taken at the Dwelling house late of Hopkin Phillip situated at Trewyda in the parish of Langovelach Liberty Aforsaid this tenth day of October In this Year of our Lord 1754 Before Gabriel Powell Gent Coroner to our Sovereign Lord the Kingwithin the Liberty Aforus & on that View of this Body of the said Hopkin Phillip Collier found Dead within the said Liberty upon the Oaths of Richard Aubrey, David Howells, John Reaper, Cornelius Waen, Griffith Williams, Edward David, Thomas Morris, John David, David Phillips, Thomas Williams, Walter Owen, Benjamin David, William David, John Morgan, David Rees, James Evan, Tho.Robert, Mathew Thomas and Edward David Good & Lawfull men of y. Liberty aforus.

& who being Sworn & Charged how & in what manner the said Came to his Death Do Say upon their Oaths That Richard Lockwood Esq. & Company are & for Some time past have been Lots of sod of a Certain Coalwork Situated at Clyndu. In parcel Clase within the said parish of Langovelach & Liberty aforus, which was near to & adjoined to a Certain Coalwork Carried on under a Tenement of Lands called Tyr Ych Fawr hool from where is the said Coalwork of Richard Lockwood Esq & Co. Was usually Supplyed with Air & that said Coalwork under Tyr Ych Lawr hool being Shut Up So that air was prevented Circulating in the Coalwork of the said Richard Lockwood Esq. & Co. and that the said Deceased had been a working collier of the said Richard Lockwood Esq. & Co. and Going on the Ninth Instant into the said Coalwork of the said Richard Lockwood Esq. & Company he was for want of Air then & there Instantly Suffocated & Dyed. So the Jurors Aforus on their Oaths Do Say That the Deceased Hopkin Phillip Came to his Death in Manner Aforus & by being Accidentally Suffocated and not otherwise to their knowledge. In writing whereof the Jurors Aforus & As well as the said Coroner have hereunto Set their hands and seals The Day and Year first above.
Gab. Powell Coroner.
Liberty of Gower in the County of Glamorgan."[3]

(Note the wax thumb seals of the Jurors are contained at the foot of the document, which suggests they were illiterate.)

The Coroner came to the conclusion the cause of death was due to an Air Ventilation shaft (*hool*) which had been shut up:

"*Was usually Supplyed with Air & that said Coalwork under Tyr Ych Lawr hool being Shut Up So that air was prevented Circulating in the Coalwork of the said Richard Lockwood Esq. & Co. and that the said Deceased had been a working collier of the said Richard Lockwood Esq. & Co.*"

Following the Inquest, the Coroner, Gabriel Powell, a Swansea Lawyer, who had in 1728 been appointed as Coroner in Gower and Kilvey, co. Glamorgan, wrote to the Duke of Beaufort, the

Lord of the Manor of Trewydda who, apart from the common land, also claimed the bed of the river Tawe and its fishing rights for two miles above the tidal point, and prohibited mining the river bed and the throwing of a bridge from bank to bank except upon payment of rent or way levee (the original grammar of the letter has not been changed):

"*2 January 1755*

My Lord Duke
I did myself the honour by last post to acquaint your Grace of Mr. J. Price again stressing the Agrais of the Coroner, with I hope your Grace has owined.

Those individuals I Informed at the Quarter Sessions are not at your Grace's prosecution, but for nuisances in the Highway, wth, will In So in measures have the same effect, as if will dates, them from doing any acts of ownership there, but so not having been since with him not to make their Submission, so that I have but one Person now for Indict.- Mr Popkin's, and ww2 was sent by a Purpose of anger to London from where In Support he will move this next term to Dissolve the Injunction wth.and Shall Showingly oppose, but whatever will be the Event, we Shall Partly know my Lord Chancellor's opinion upon the matter. – The trespassers I have said in the Declaration agt. in Popkin are only Some trifling Trespassers & on and upon the Commons with his Carts, one, and Fishing in the River. We are not obliged to Prove every Trespass charged; one is enough to obtain an Affadavit and therefore if those should arise Aug Difficulty in Argument to Cutting the Trees. A verdict may perhaps be Secured for one of the other Trespassers.

The affair of Thomas Price, I believe was not mentioned to your Grace in a letter, but only given in amongst the complaints of encroachments committed on the commons [surrounding Trewydda] A few months will make no great differences, but I was afraid of this.

Gain a title by Length of Time – Mr, Price took so much pains in stopping the air from Mr. Morris's Works and did it effortually, that he has for the present soly destroyed his own, and will not be able to recover them without being at a very great expense. He has already made

several attempts but all to no purpose and by news of the last new Pit,
Mr Morris will be able to work his coal for the future quite independ-
ent of him- The Indictment against Mr. Price's Workman for him poi-
soning Mr. Morris's. Does not belong to the same suit as that against
John Jones, it is before. Ours was at Treboeth Work; but the work-
man that was, had been employed to keep open the air holes which Mr.
Price had so Effortually shut up that the Fellows lost their lives and
Mr. Morris was prevented Working near four months and by with he
himself works. The reason for removing flues Indictment to the Court
of Kings Bench is because it will be better to stay at Hereford than at
Our Quarter Sessions, and the Prosecutors, if they succeed, will receive
much greater satisfaction.

Mr. Morris has been alarmed within these few days with the fires reviv-
ing in Mr.Powell's coal works and is preparing to turn down water again,
with if they do we will probably be again smoke't out of the Treboath
work, but upon speaking to Mr. Powell's agents they admit that this fire
not having been put quite out, had by some means or other rekindled,
and is not clear that John Jones has not clandestinely got into the work.
They will spare no labour or expense to extinquish it effectually and
if behooves him to do so, for at present their own work seems to be in
most danger.

I am,
My Lord,
Your Grace's most Dutiful
& obedient Servant.
Gab. Powell."

The grammar of the letter has not been changed.

Apart from dealing with issues of trespass on the Duke's land, the main thrust of the letter deals with an injunction on the actions of Thomas Price and his workmen. The indictment levelled against Thomas Price and his workmen was for poisoning Mr Morris' fellow miners and preventing him from using the mine for many months, suggesting that coal production took precedent over miners' lives and their families. There were also problems with an unattended fire at Gabriel Powell's colliery, which was causing smoke at John Morris's Treboeth colliery. With the death of the Duke in 1756, proceedings were stopped before the plaintiffs were due to file their answers. We have no evidence to show whether or not the Indictment was dealt with in court or withdrawn.[4]

In the next chapter we will look at the emergence of Graig Trewyddfa's coal industry and the heart-breaking working conditions of men, women and children employed in cutting the coal prior to Children's Employment Commission's Report of 1842 and subsequent legislation.

CHAPTER II
BIBLIOGRAPHY AND ILLUSTRATIONS

(1) National Library of Wales Badmington Papers II 2377
(2) Ibid
(3) Ibid
(4) Ibid

(Plate 1) Coroner's Handwritten Report on the death of 'Hopkin Phillip 'who resided at Trewyddfa, Morriston. 10 October 1754. Courtesy National Library of Wales Badmington Papers II

CHAPTER III

THE EMERGENCE OF GRAIG TREWYDDFA'S COAL INDUSTRY AND THE WORKING CONDITIONS OF MEN, WOMEN AND CHILDREN EMPLOYED IN THE MINES

The area which abounds Cwm Burlais, Treboeth, Brynhyfryd, Landore, Plasmarl and Morriston was commonly known as Graig Trewyddfa. It was rich in bituminous coal, and below ground were lucrative veins of coal of the best quality for copper smelting, known as the Five Foot Great Penvilian, which was the closest to the surface and could be mined easily with levels and slants, and the deeper Six Foot, Three Foot and Two Foot seams requiring vertical shafts. Coal extraction had sprung up in the lower Swansea Valley in the 18th century, so it was inevitable that copper masters would take an interest in the business of coal mining. So did landowners, who realised they were sitting on a fortune.

The coal levels west of the river Tawe could reach the Great Penvilan Five Foot seam, but miners were occasionally faced with synclines (a steep underground valleys) and anticlines (a steep underground hills) which the coal seam would follow. However, deep shafts from the surface were required to work the lower bituminous coal seams.

At the beginning of the 19th century methods of coal extraction were primitive. The general methods used for coal extraction during this period ranged in size from the early bell pits, a few metres in diameter, dug down to a seam at shallow depth, to 'slants or drifts' that followed the dip of the coal seams into the hillside, providing water drainage and saving on the costs of pumping gear. Occasionally the drifts were extensive, but as involved higher costs for haulage, it was usually cheaper to drive a fresh drift into the hillside than extend an existing one, even though there might have been plenty of coal left. The collieries were generally small and each had a separate owner and mining employees. As a result the Graig Trewydda hillsides were riddled with tunnels. (See Plate 1)

(Plate 1) Remains of old coal level at Caemawr above Tan-y-Lan Terrace, Morriston This location, overlooking the Tawe valley, has since been cleared and re-developed with housing.
March 1960 SS 665979 (c) J.P.Thomas

It was claimed at the time, in a conversation the author had with a veteran miner, Johnny Williams of Morfydd Street, who worked the lower seams at Copper Pit, that because of the absence of a mining geologist, the drift broke out on the escarpment above Morriston, causing Trewyddfa Road to partially collapse. The road had to be rebuilt using an elliptical arched bridge which remains in place today and is shown in the following photograph:

*(Plate 2) Site of collapsed Trewyddfa Road due to mining activity
and re-built using an elliptical arched bridge.
March 1960 SS665977 (c) J.P.Thomas*

The mining work force at the time was comprised of men, women and children, who laboured for long hours in dangerous conditions. Most workers started their shifts between 5am and 6am and worked a twelve-hour day. It was usual to work six days a week, with days off on Sundays and holy days and the occasional 'treat day' if there was a big national or local event. After a breakfast of bread and milk, or porridge, they would walk – often several miles – to the pithead. Underground workers were transported down the shaft, then had to walk to the coalface along low, narrow, roadways. It was pitch-black underground with no light apart from tallow candles (which the miners had to buy themselves) until the introduction of lamps. These were first used in the early 19th century, but their introduction was gradual and not universal.

In 1841, about 216,000 people were employed in the mines of Great Britain. However, women and children worked underground the same long hours as men, but for smaller wages. The public became aware of conditions in the country's collieries in 1838 after an accident at Huskar Colliery in Silkstone, near Barnsley. A stream overflowed into the ventilation drift after violent thunderstorms causing the death of 26 children; 11 girls aged from 8 to 16 and 15 boys between 9 and 12 years of age. The disaster came to the attention of Queen Victoria, who ordered an inquiry.[1]

Coal seams varied in thickness from 18 inches to Five or Six Foot in the Swansea district, which meant the miners worked in very confined spaces. Where possible, pit ponies were used to carry the coal. However, in narrow seams, women and children had the job of carrying the coal while crawling on their hands and knees. Children were sometimes chained, belted, harnessed to a coal cart, black, saturated with wet, and more than half-naked – crawling upon their hands and feet, and dragging their heavy loads behind them.[2]

The Victorians saw child labour as a normal part of working life. Most children started work underground when they were around eight years old, but some were as young as five. They would work the same hours as adults, sometimes longer, at jobs that paid far less. Indeed, it was quite common for whole families to work together underground to earn enough money for the family to live on. There existed a division of labour within the family workforce:

THE TRAPPER – The trapper was often the youngest member of the family working underground. Their job was simple: to open and close the wooden doors (trap doors) that allowed fresh air to flow through the mine. They would usually sit in total darkness for up to twelve hours at a time, waiting to let the coal tub through the door. It was not hard work but it was boring and could be very dangerous. If they fell asleep, the safety of the whole workings could be affected.[3]

THE HURRIER AND THE THRUSTER – The older children and women were employed as hurriers, pulling and pushing tubs full of coal along roadways from the coal face to the pit-bottom. The younger children usually worked in pairs, one as a hurrier, the other as a thruster, but the older children and women worked alone.

(Plate 3) Hurriers and Thrusters at work moving coal. Courtesy of the Commission of Enquiry into the State of Children in Employment in 1842.

Hurriers would be harnessed to the tub, and thrusters would help hurriers by pushing the tubs of coal from behind with their hands and the tops of their heads. The tubs and the coal could weigh over 600kg, and would have to be moved through roadways which were often only 60–120 cm high.

THE GETTER – Getters were the oldest and strongest members of the family, almost always grown men or strong youths. Their job was to work at the coal face cutting the coal from the seam with a pickaxe. This work was usually preceded by drilling holes for explosive charges to loosen the coal, often laying on their side using their elbow as a pivot, whence follow inflammations of the joint, and in cases where he is forced to kneel, of the knee also.

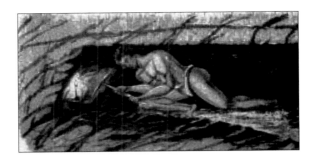

(Plate 4) Getter (Collier) working a coal seam.
Courtesy of the Commission of Enquiry into the
State of Children in Employment in 1842.

There was no mechanised mining during this this period and drilling for explosive charges was a difficult task, particularly in the narrower seams, and was described as shown here:

"It follows that a knowledge of how to place the holes so as to allow the powder the best show to do the maximum of work is necessary to the ordinary miner. A good blow at the right place will accomplish more than half a dozen at a wrong one. The holes for the powder are bored with a drill. The drill is a bar of steel from one to five feet long of octagonal section, so as to give a better grip for the hand than if it were round. These drills are usually seven eighths of an inch in diameter. The sharp end of the drill, called a bit, is a cutter with a sharp edge and two angular corners. In drilling a man holds the drill in one hand and turns it round and round, while at each turn he gives a blow on the head of the drill with a hammer, which he holds in his other hand."[4]

This hand-drilling process was arduous, demanding and tiring. Getters were the only members of the family who would work continually with a candle or safety lamp, as they needed the light to see the coal face. Getters had to buy their own candles, usually made from tallow or animal fat.

However, carbonic acid gas, which also develops in great quantities, accumulates in the deeper parts of the mine, frequently reaching the height of a man, and suffocates every one who gets into it. The doors which separate the sections of the mines are meant to prevent the propagation of explosions and the movement of the gases; but since they are entrusted to small children, who often fall asleep or neglect them, this means of prevention is illusory. A proper ventilation of the mines by means of fresh air-shafts could almost entirely remove the injurious effects of both these gases. But for this purpose the mine owner has no money to spare, preferring to command the working-men to use the Davy lamp, which was found to have limited use because of its dull light, and was, therefore, usually replaced by a candle.

Interestingly, a miners' lamp unique to South Wales, and including the Swansea district, was the ball and peg lamp invented by Arthur Morris of Aberdare, South Wales. It was manufactured of either steel or brass, or a combination of both, dating from at least the 1850s through to the early 1900s. The cost of manufacturing these lamps were considerably less that that of the Davy design, but were designed to be used in 'well-ventilated' pits. However, they were no defence against pockets or concentrations of methane gas, which could appear unexpectantly at the coal face, resulting in explosions. Morris' ball and peg lamp was not patented until 1894.

(Plate 5) Examples of designs of Miners' Ball and Peg Lamps.
Courtesy David Johnson and Manfred Stutzer

The lamps were all manufactured with screw threads at the top and bottom of the spherical fuel font. A closed–end threaded tube could be screwed to the base to serve as a handle, or screwed over the burner to protect the wick, and allow the lamp to be carried in the pocket without leaking. These lamps could be carried in the hand and reportedly attached to the miner's cap through the use of a loop on the cap tp hold the handle. These oil lamps attached to a miners cap would have stood up higher than the better-known oilwick cap lamps, making them inconvenient in low-headroom mines. Morris' patent included a sealed matchsafe in the handle of the lamp, along with a knurled match striker encircling the handle.[5] If an explosion occured, the recklessness of the miner was usually blamed, though the mineowner could have made the explosion well–nigh impossible by supplying good ventilation. Furthermore, every few days the roof of a working would fall in, and bury or mangle the workers employed in it. It was the interest of the mine owner to have the seams worked out as completely as possible, and hence accidents of this sort occured. Then, too, the ropes by which the men descend into the mines were often rotten, and would snap, so that the unfortunates would fall, and and get crushed.

The following table shows the causes of deaths in coal mining accidents, particularly among young children:

Cause of Death.	Under 13 years of age.	13 and not exceeding 18 years of age.	Above 18 years of age.
Fell down the shafts	13	16	31
Fell down the shaft from the rope breaking	1	..	2
Fell out when ascending	..	..	3
Drawn over the pulley	3	..	3
Fall of stone out of a skip down the shaft	1	..	3
Drowned in the mines	3	4	15
Fall of stones, coal, and rubbish in the mines	14	14	69
Injuries in coal-pits, the nature of which is not specified	6	3	32
Crushed in coal-pits	..	1	1
Explosion of gas	13	18	49
Suffocated by choke-damp	..	2	6
Explosion of gunpowder	..	1	3
By tram-waggons	4	5	12
Total	58	62	229

(Plate 6) Table listing the number and causes of deaths
of children and adults in a coal mine.
Courtesy Childrens Employment Commission (Mines) 1842.

We can see from this table that the highest number of deaths among childen under the age of 13 were caused by 'falling down pit shafts', 'falling of stones and other debris' and 'gas explosions'.

Until the The Commission of Enquiry into the State of Children in Employment in 1842 mid-nineteenth century, the British state accepted that children as young as five years old were an acceptable part of the industrial workforce and many worked in horrific conditions in coal mines. Not only did management accepted the position but many parents as well. Between 1840 and 1842 government inspectors visited the Welsh coalfields and spoke to many child miners. Not only management accept the position, many parents did as well. These interviews were presented to Parliament as part of the Enquiry and were deeply shocking.

Many people had no idea that coal was excavated by young children. But it was the immorality rather than the cruelty of the mines that shocked them most. There follows an illustrated page from the Report concerning the degrading use of young female hurriers. The Commissioner has not minced his words:

.... the *First Report of the Children's Employment Commission, on Mines* which was published in 1842 and led to Parliament passing the Coalmines Regulation Act in the same year, under the terms of which the employment of women and girls underground in coal mines was forbidden. The evidence presented in this report brought into the light of day scenes which not only exposed the cruel misuse of women and children in mines, but also revealed indecency on a staggering scale. Girls were to be seen half-naked, with their breasts exposed. One of the Sub-Commissioners reported that 'One of the most disgusting sights I have ever seen was that of young females, dressed like boys in trousers, crawling on all fours, with belts round their waists, and chains passing between their legs' as they drew loaded wagons along mine passages.' The Report was unusual in that it was illustrated ....

    The Sub-Commissioner, Mr. Thomas Peace, told of Harriet Morton: 'an intelligent girl, who seemed to feel the degradation of her lot so keenly that it was quite painful to take her evidence.' No detail was spared the reader: 'The chain, passing high up between the legs of two of these girls, had worn large holes in their trousers, and any sight more disgustingly indecent or revolting can scarcely be imagined than these girls at work. No brothel can beat it.'[7]

(Plate 7) Drawing of a young girl pulling a cart of coal fitted with towing chain and girdle 1842. The Commission of Enquiry into the State of Children in Employment 1842. Courtesy Michael Hiley.

"As to their sexual relations, men, women, and children work in the mines, in many cases, wholly naked, and in most cases, nearly so, by reason of the prevailing heat, and the consequences in the dark, lonely mines may be imagined. The number of illegitimate children is here disproportionately large, and indicates what goes on among the half-savage population below ground; but proves too, that the illegitimate intercourse of the sexes has not here, as in the great cities, sunk to the level of prostitution."[6]

In south Wales at the time, coal was sold by the wey of 6 Chaldrons or 216 Bushels (about ten tonnes) at a price of two pounds and nine shillings per wey. Culm which consisted of the shiverings of the coal found in the extremity of the veins, and used by smiths and lime-burners, was sold considerably cheaper at thirty to fourty shillings per weigh. It was a lucrative trade for both landlords and mine owners.

Mining was dirty, difficult and dangerous and conditions underground were cramped and particularly perilous. Some mines were hot and wet – others hot and dusty – and underground workers often worked naked or semi-naked. Ventilation was poor and water sometimes seeped in through the rocks above and gathered in old workings. Flooding was always a possibility and an ever-present fear. Accidents and cause of injury or death and shaft accidents were also common, while mine gases could cause explosions or poison the workers. Few colliers reached the age of 30 without suffering respiratory problems and, in the 1840s, it was accepted that it was rare for them to live beyond their early 50s. Perhaps for those who did it was largely because the mining community was noted for its tremendous camaraderie.

At the coalface the collier worked in an area no taller than the height of the seam, which was often less than 60cm and lit by a single candle. The coal was then shovelled into large baskets or small carts which were then pulled and pushed to the bottom of the shaft. This was sometimes done by older children, although ponies might be used for parts of the journey when space permitted.

Deformities were common among children who worked in the mines, with conditions such as 'stunted growth', 'crippled gait' and 'irritation of head, back and feet' all being recorded.

Many suffered skin sores resulting from the wearing of the girdles used to attach them to the wagons, although this practice had been largely discontinued by the 1860s. A surgeon, who made a submission to the Children's Employment Commission, reported that most of the children were asthmatic by the age of 20 and that respiratory diseases were common – disorders no doubt exacerbated by the living conditions of the time. injuries were a common occurrence. Roof-falls were probably the commonest.[7]

Evan Daniel, employed as a Surveyor to the Swansea Coal Company, which owned several mines in the Swansea district, appeared as a witness in the Employment Commission of 1842, inquiring into the Employment of Children in Mines and Manufacture, where it was alleged he was making a rather bad use of the maxim *"Train up a child [for coal mining activities]"*. His evidence to the Commission provides a useful account of the use of child labour in the Swansea district's mines:

"In the works under their charge, when the distance is great, they employ horses to bring the coal to the mainways. In other places they employ boys from 15 to 18 years of age. No children draw with the girdle and chain, none of this class being required in the works, but strong boys frequently convey or push the coals in the wagons 200 or 300 yards and work two together when required. The weight of the loaded carriages is about 15 cwt. each. The coals are brought to the surface by steam power applied to the pits and by horses applied to the trams in the levels. A few female adults are employed in taking out the slate at the surface and on the far department. The children are generally taken to work from 8 to 12 years old. The youngest children are taken in to open and shut air doors, etc. The parent looks after work for the child every day. We think 12 years would be a very proper age for boys to begin to work in this district. We observe that they are very healthy but of a small size. They generally work about eight hours. In some of the works they work two sets, when they relieve each other about four o'clock and work till midnight. Children work fully as long as the adults. A very limited number are employed at night."[8]

(Plate 8) Group of young coal miners. Courtesy of A. Venning.

The employment of young children in coal mines was common practice across south Wales:

- Mary Davis was a 'pretty little girl' of six years old. The Government Inspector found her fast asleep against a large stone underground in the Plymouth Mines, Merthyr. After being wakened she said: *"I went to sleep because my lamp had gone out for want of oil. I was frightened for someone had stolen my bread and cheese. I think it was the rats."*
- Susan Reece, also six years of age and a door keeper in the same colliery said: *"I have been below six or eight months and I don't like it much. I come here at six in the morning and leave at six at night. When my lamp goes out, or I am hungry, I run home. I haven't been hurt yet."*

Even the simple matter of getting to their place of work was sometimes highly dangerous. Many mines were 'drifts' driven into the mountainside and children could walk in; others were shafts, which were served by winches or steam engines. The mines in the Llanelli area were up to 500 feet deep and had to be descended into by baskets, ladders, or by two persons sitting crosslegged on a suspended beam.

(Plate 9) An illustration from 1842 Commissioners'
Report showing woman lowering two children down a mine shaft

Philip Philip, aged 10, from Brace Colliery in Llanelli, was accustomed to the dangers of ladders: "I help my brother to cart. I can go down the ladders by myself. I am not afraid to go down the pit."

The inspector who interviewed Philip climbed down these ladders with difficulty. Unlike Philip, he was afraid of the noise and the heavy pumping rods that were very close to the ladders.

Edward Edwards aged 9, of Yskyn Colliery, Briton Ferry, told an Inspector:

"My employment is to cart coals from the head to the main road; the distance is 60 yards; there are no wheels to the carts {weighing about 1. ½ cwt of coal}; I push them before me; sometimes I drag them, as the cart sometimes is pulled on us, and we get crushed often."

Children, mainly boys as young as eight, worked as breakers. Here, the coal was crushed, washed, and sorted according to size. The coal would come down a chute and along a moving belt. These breaker boys would work in what was called the picking room. Here, they would work hunched over for ten hours a day, six days a week, sorting the rock and slate from the coal with their bare hands. If their attention drifted for even a second, they could lose a finger in the machinery. The work also resulted in their exposure to a large amount of dust. In some cases, the dust was so dense that their vision would be obstructed. This dust would also get into their lungs, which, needless to say, was terrible for their health. These children sometimes even had a person prodding or kicking them into obedience to make sure their attention did not stray.[9]

It appears that the employment of young children in Tinplate Works was also common practice across south Wales, as shown in the following picture:

(Plate 10) Workers at an unidentified Swansea District Tinplate Works. Note the child labourers on the left of the photograph including a young girl wearing clogs. Courtesy Wetherspoons.

Mines and Collieries Act 1842 (c. 99), commonly known as the Mines Act 1842, was an act of the Parliament of the United Kingdom. It prohibited all women and girls, and boys under ten years old, from working underground in coal mines, although Parish apprentices between the ages of 10 and 18 could continue to work in the mines. It was a response to the working conditions of children revealed in the Children's Employment Commission (Mines) 1842 report. There was no compensation for those made unemployed, which caused much hardship. The Commission was headed by Lord Anthony Ashley-Cooper, 7th Earl of Shaftesbury.

However, the Bill remained a dead letter in most districts, because no mine inspectors were appointed to watch over its being carried into effect. In fact, there was only one inspector to cover the whole of Britain, and he had to give prior notice before visiting collieries.[10] Therefore many women probably carried on working illegally for several years, their presence only being revealed when they were killed or injured. So in single cases the employment of women may have been discontinued, but in general the old state of things remained as before; it was not until the mid-19th century that children were limited to a 12-hour day. Later in 1880, the Compulsory Education Act helped reduce the numbers of child labourers, and subsequent laws raised their age and made working conditions safer.

However, these mid-nineteenth century degrading employment concerns did not hinder the development of the local coal industry at Graig Trewyddfa, which the copper smelters were dependent upon.

Major players in the quest for the 'Holy Grail' were the Morris family of Morriston, their partner Thomas Lockwood, the Vivian family, the Richard Calvert Jones family of Swansea, the Price family of Penllegaer, and the Glasbrook family, whose chequered coal mining interests were mainly located to the west of Swansea at Cwm Burlais, Berthlwydd, Garngoch and the Cwmdulais Valley. Latecomers were Edward Daniels and John Jenkins of the Cwmfelin Tinplate Works which opened two collieries near Llangyfelach as late as 1887. However, as previously stated, so intensively was the area mined, however, and for so long, it is difficult to establish an exact record of the various undertakings and, in some cases, to differentiate from one undertaking from another.[11]

Likewise, if we peruse the following map showing the principal coal pits or levels, their tramroads and owners existing in and around Graig Trewyddfa during the eighteenth and nineteenth centuries, a clearer chronology of their individual developments, their contribution to the district's copper smelting industry and the precarious working conditions that miners faced in the quest for the'holy grail', should emerge.

(Plate 11) Map originally produced by Swansea History Project No.4. (not to scale) showing principal coal pits, levels, and tramroads in and around Graig Trewyddfa during 18th and 19th centuries. It should be noted that prior to 1809, a single company 'Lockwood, Morris & Co'. existed. John Morris then withdrew from the partnership and established the Penvilia Vein Company. The tramroads coloured red, green, blue and orange and other mines have been inserted by the author. Courtesy Swansea Reference Library.

It was during this period of early coal extraction that John Morris, son of Robert Morris, was planning his new coal level at Clyndu; there was already a mine in operation called the 'Clyndu Water Machine Pit' sited to the west of Vicarage Road opposite its junction with Cwmbath Road. Here the water pump and the winding gear were powered by an undershot water wheel engine. There were no millponds in the vincinity to provide a fast flowing water leat to operate the machinery, so Lockwood, Morris & Co constructed a long underground drainage canal from Clase Bach diverting water to the 'Clyndu Water Machine Pit'. The coal workings of this pit had extended its headings northwards towards the Penvilia Five Foot Seam and can be seen on an 1830 mining map tracing of Graig Trewydda showing the routes of the 'Canal Underground Formerly' and 'Clyndu Level Colliery' from its entrance, in Uplands Terrace, to Llangyfelach via the Clyndu Water Machine Pit. Unfortunately, the map was drawn on heavy grey tracing paper, making reproduction difficult, so it was necessary to enhance the image on the drawing paper to reveal the detail.

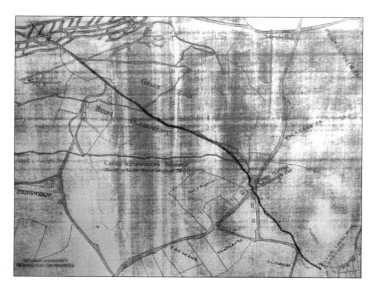

(Plate 12) Part section of 1830 grey map tracing showing mining activity under Graig Trewydda, Morriston. Morris's Clyndu Level and its Penvilia Seam workings are shown in RED and the' Canal Underground Formally' taking water to the Machine Pit is shown in BLUE. Public Surface Roadways are shown in ORANGE. The author has named the surface roadways and the Clyndu Level Mine Entrance which can be seen at the bottom right hand corner. Courtesy, Swansea Univerity Library, Richard Burton Archives. Ref: LAC/95/A/1

Interestingly, the map shows the 'Ruins of Clasemont House' (Plate 3), demolished in 1822 when John Morris took up residence at Sketty Park, in Derwyn Fawr, Swansea. It is said that he removed all the fine monumental stone work and fixtures of value from Clasemont House in one night to facilitate the building of his Sketty Park Estate, part of which still stands today; hence the building is marked as 'ruins'.

(Plate 13) William Booth's 1770's Painting of John Morris with his gun and retriever dog at Clasemont House overlooking Morriston and the Swansea Valley. SS 663986 Courtesy Bristol Museum

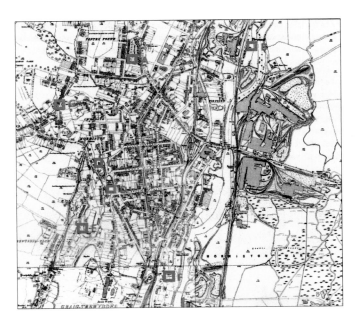

(Plate 14) Map of past Morriston district coal mines. 'A' Pentrepoeth, 'B' Tircanol, 'C' Clyndu Level, 'D' Fiery Coalery, 'E' Level y Graig, 'F' Copper Pit, 'G' Water Machine Pit.
(Note the map does not show the later Pen-rhiw-felen and Brynwilach collieries sited near Llangyfelach) Courtesy O.H.M.S.

Edward Martin, Mining Engineer and Principal Mining Surveyor to the Duke of Beaufort, had observed the best methods used for mining the rich reserves of coal in south Wales:[12]

"The veins of coal and iron ore, in the vincinity of most of the iron works in Monmouthshire and Glamorganshire, are drained and worked by levels or horizontal drifts, which opportunity is given by the deep valleys which generally run in a north and south direction, intersecting the range of coal and iron ore, which run in an east and west direction, under the high mountains, and thereby serving as main drains, so that the collier or miner here gets at the treasures of the earth, without going to the expense and labour of sinking deep pits, and erecting powerful fire-engines."

It followed that coal levels or drifts could be constructed with slight rising gradient inwards from the entrance, allowing underground mine water to drain away from the coal face to the mine entrance and beyond. The gradient also provided a bed for a tramway to remove the mined coal to the level entrance. However, deep shafts from the surface were required to work the lower bitiminous coal seams, with the erection of fire-engines to operate minewater pumps.

In the following chapter we will take a close look at the main collieries in the Morriston district, which worked the Five Foot Penvilia Vein and supplied bituminous coal to the developing copper smelting industries. These were the historic Clyndu Level, Tircanol, Clyndu Water Machine Pit, and Hen Lefel y Graig (Park). The Fire Engine Coalery and Copper Pit generally worked the lower seams. There were also a few smaller and unnamed pits, for example, at Cwmrhydyceirw and Pentrepoeth, which mined varying amounts of coal.

CHAPTER III
BIBLIOGRAPHY AND ILLUSTRATIONS

(1) 'The Employment Commission into the Employment of Children in Mines and Manufacture'. 1842

(2) Ibid

(3) Ibid

(4) Eureka, The Journal of Mining Collectibles Issue 46 Part II January 2015. 'How mining is done' pp 17–22

(5) Ibid. 'Lamps'. pp 12–15

(6) Taken from *The Condition of the Working Class in England in 1844*: Friedrich Engels (1845). [*It is likely that these conditions also applied to collieries in south Wales.*]

(7) 'The Employment Commission into the Employment of Children in Mines and Manufacture'. 1842. Evidence given by Evan, Daniel Surveyor, Swansea Coal Company. P.115 [*Evan Daniel served his apprenticeship with the Penclawdd Canal & Railway or Tramroad Company under the* direction *of Edward Martin and David Davies.*]

(8) The Employment Commission into the Employment of Children in Mines and Manufacture'. 1842

(9) Ibid.

(10) National Museum of Wales, Article 2011–04–11.

(11) Treboeth Historical and Pictorial Record. Treboeth Historical Society p.125

(12) Description of the Mineral Basin in the Counties of Monmouth, Glamorgan, Brecon, Carmarthen and Pembroke, Edward Martin, Philisophical Transactions of the Royal Society of London Vol 96 (1806) pp. 344–345

(Plate 1) Remains of old coal level at Caemawr above Tan-y-Lan Terrace, Morriston This location, overlooking the Tawe valley, has since been cleared and re-developed with housing. March 1960 SS 665979 (c) J.P.Thomas

(Plate 2) Site of collapsed Trewyddfa Road due to mining activity and re-built using an elliptical arched bridge. March 1960 SS665977 (c) J.P.Thomas

(Plate 3) Hurriers and Thrusters at work moving coal. Courtesy. Commission of Enquiry into the State of Children in Employment in 1842

(Plate 4) Getter (Collier) working a coal seam. Courtesy. Commission of Enquiry into the State of Children in Employment in 1842

(Plate 5) Examples of designs of Miners' Ball and Peg Lamps. Courtesy David Johnson and Manfred Stutzer

(Plate 6) Table listing numbers of deaths of people working in a coal mine by various causes. Courtesy Childrens Employment Commission (Mines) 1842. p.537.

(Plate 7) Drawing of a young girl puliing a cart of coal fitted with towing chain and girdle 1842. The Commission of Enquiry into the State of Children in Employment 1842. Courtesy Michael Hiley

(Plate 8) Group of young coal miners. Courtesy of A. Venning.

(Plate 9) An illustration from 1842 Commissioners' Report showing woman lowering two children down a mine shaft

(Plate 10) Workers at an unknown Swansea District Tinplate Works. Note the child labourers to the left of the photograph. The young girl is wearing clogs. Picture displayed at Red Lion Restaurant, Morriston, Swansea. (1 July 2018) J.P.Thomas. Courtesy Wetherspoons.

(Plate 11) Map originally produced by Swansea History Project No.4.(not to scale) showing principal coal pits, levels, and tramroads in and around Graig Trewyddfa during 18th and 19th centuries. It should be noted that prior to 1809, a single company 'Lockwood, Morris & Co'. existed. John Morris then withdrew from the partnership and established the Penvilia Vein Company. The tramroads coloured red, green, blue and orange and other mines have been inserted by the author. Courtesy Swansea Reference Library

(Plate 12) Part section of 1830 grey map tracing showing mining activity under Graig Trewyddfa, Morriston. Morris's Clyndu Level and its Penvilia Seam workings are shown in RED and the' Canal Underground Formally' taking water to the Machine Pit is shown in BLUE. Public Surface Roadways are shown in ORANGE. The author has named the surface roadways and the Clyndu Level Mine Entrance which can be seen at the bottom right hand corner. Courtesy, Swansea Univerity Library, Richard Burton Archives. Ref: LAC/95/A/1

(Plate 13) William Booth's 1770's Painting of John Morris with his gun and retriever dog at Clasemont House overlooking Morriston and the Swansea Valley. SS 663986

(Plate 14) Map of past Morriston district coal mines. 'A' Pentrepoeth, 'B' Tircanol, 'C' Clyndu Level, 'D' Fiery Coalery, 'E' Level y Graig, 'F' Copper Pit, 'G' Water Machine Pit. Courtesy O.H.M.S.

CHAPTER IV

CLYNDU LEVEL COLLIERY AND TRAMWAY

In all probability the Clyndu Level Colliery was opened by Lockwood Morris & Co. in 1747–48, since this date coincides with the building of the Forest Copperworks. However, in a letter of November 1753, sent by Gabriel Powell to the Duke of Beaufort he reported that John Morris had at last been fortunate to discover the 'Great Penvilia Coal Vein' in its full perfection at the bottom of Trewyddfa Common, just above the copper-works.[1] The Penvilia vein was a contemporary name for the five-foot seam, which is the vein which the Clyndu Level Colliery worked, and the location given by Gabriel Powell corresponds to the location of the level. (See Plate 3)

(Plate 1) Aerial View of Site of Clyndu Level Colliery Entrance, Uplands Terrace, Morriston. The houses are built on the site of the Clyndu Level Colliery pony stables. February 2017. SS 664981 National Library of Scotland

The level entrance, measuring eight feet high and almost four feet and seven inches wide, was driven northwesterly into the bowels of Graig Trewyddfa some eleven hundred yards until reaching Llangyfelach. From its entrance in Uplands Terrace, Morriston (Plate 6), adjacent to the public footpath, the level eventually joined up with the Clyndu Water Machine Pit which at the time was mining and transporting coal for the Forest Copperworks using a cart-road. This link-up enabled this coal to be transported to the Copperworks using the newly opened Clyndu Level wagonway instead of the inefficient cart-road where the carts tended to turn tracks into muddy quagmires.

Beyond the water machine pit engine shaft, the level curved to the west along the dip of the Swansea Five-Foot seam as it dropped steeply almost from the crest of Craig Trewyddfa. "By 1796 workings had proceeded 260 yards beyond the shaft and along the width of the seam, the tunnel already ran westwards some 820 yards across the seam. The main passage continued another 660 yards as a dry heading until halted by a fault almost under Llangyfelach Road."[2] The form and length of the level can be identified from a 1830s map tracing of mine workings under Graig Trewyddfa. (Plate 3)

Moreover, it is likely that the Clyndu Level was driven into the Trewydda hillside at a slight upward incline (which was common mining practice in south Wales at the time) to provide a natural drain for the coal levels instead of installing expensive water pumps, as well as a way of moving the coal out of the colliery by carts or tramway: Graig Trewyddfa was notorious for its mine-water and flooding, so much so that in 1909 Swansea Corporation decided to use this natural water supply to construct an underground storage reservoir to serve the Morriston township. (This is discussed later in this chapter)

The Clyndu Level was worked by small trams, which were taken in and out of the level by horse tramroad. The coal came out at Ty-Coch, near the present entrance of Bath Villa, whence it was taken down to the Forest copperworks by a wagonway.[3]

(Plate 2) Site of Entrance to Clyndu Level Colliery (now landscaped) in Uplands Terrace, Morriston. May 2012. The paved path on the right remains a public right of way leading to upper Clyndu Street. SS 666978. The tramway followed Upland Terrace to its junction with Clyndu Street. (c) J.P.Thomas.

"It is not surprising since it owes its origins to an earlier wagon-way by which coal was brought down from levels on the side of the valley... A wagonway, now Clyndu Street, was built and it ran in a *straight line from the mouth of the level to the copperworks.*"[4]

The first definite reference we have to the Clyndu waggon-way is on a map drawn by Lewis Thomas in 1761 from a survey made a few years previously. (Plate 7)

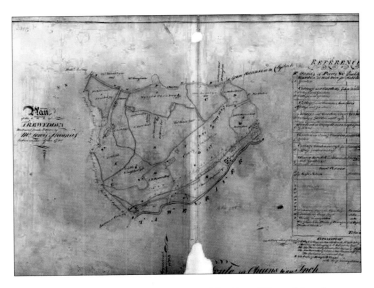

(Plate 3) Lewis Thomas's 1761 Map of the Fee of Trewydda. Courtesy West Glamorgan Archives (Badmington Collection Vol.72, Plate 27)

Thomas' map shows the level and a coal road running down to the copperworks, which is explicitly labelled as *'The road where John Morris' carts bring down the Coal to the Copper works'*. Clyndu Street follows the course of this road. The level worked the Five Foot Vein. It remained the property of Lockwood, Morris & Co and continued to be worked even after the Forest works was closed in about 1790. In 1800 John Morris recorded in his commonplace book that the daily output was eight weys (64 tons) and in 1805 the Cumbrian engineer, John Bateman, noted that the main level was 700 yards long.

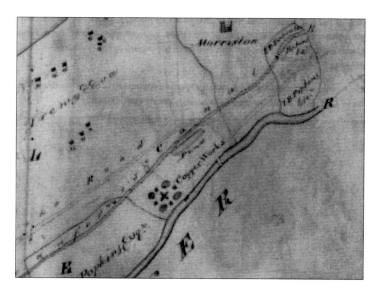

(Plate 4) Enlarged Section of Lewis Thomas's 1761 Map of the Fee of Trewyddfa showing Forest Copperworks and 'straight-line' Clyndu Tramroad (There is no reference to a Clyndu boat level canal nor a navigational canal). Note the large pond fed by a stream which crossed the canal, and later the railway line, by an aquaduct, which may have supplied water to drive the copperworks' machinery. (See Plate 12) Courtesy West Glamorgan Archives (Badmington Collection Vol.72, Plate 27)

The gradient of Clyndu Street was measured as averaging 2.5 degrees, which meant that an incline haulage engine was not required. The tramway could accommodate four or five wagons, the loaded ones descending on the brake, with an empty wagon at the end carrying one or two horses for the uphill journey with empty wagons back to the level. This method was employed by the Duke of Bridgewater's Canal to transport coal from his mines at Worsley to the industrial areas of Manchester. This practice was observed by Svedenstierna during his visit to the Landore area in 1801-2:[5]

"*The transport of coal from the nearest mines down to the ships is done over a railway specially laid for the purpose, which is laid at such a gradient that two wagons coupled together and each loaded with a chaldron (about 13 hundredweight) of coal, run forwards by their own weight, being restrained in theit journey by a brake fitted to the rear waggon, applied by a man who travels with it to deal with the unloading... The empty waggons are afterwards coupled together in a train, and hauled up over the same way by a horse.*"

(Plate 5) Descending coal waggons using the brake at Bridgewater, Manchester, 1863. CourtesyJoyce. H.M. Banks. 'A Nineteenth Century Colliery Railway, p.161, 1974.

P.R. Reynolds, in his 1976 South West Wales Industrial Archaeology Society Paper on the the Clyndu and Pentremawled Tramroads, shows the Clyndu Level wagonway, now Clyndu Street, running in a dead-straight line from the mouth of the level to the copperworks (Plate 10).

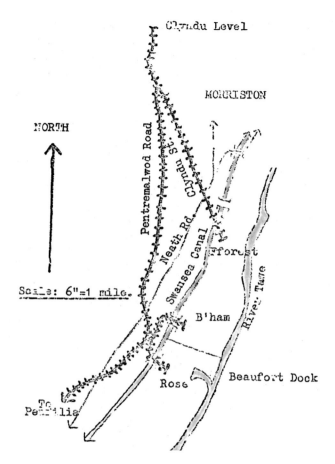

(Plate 6) P.R. Reynold's 1975 Map of the routes of the Clyndu Street and Pentremawled Tramroads. Note the straight line of the route to the Forest copperworks which crossed the later Trewyddfa Canal by means of a bridge. The blue colouring of the Trewyddfa/ Swansea Canal and the river Tawe has been added by the Author. Courtesy South West Wales Industrial Archaeology Society.

(Plate 7) View of upper Clyndu Street looking downwards from junction with Uplands Terrace (left) where the Clyndu Level entrance was sited. The junction on the right is Pentremawled Road where a tramroad was later constructed. December 2016 SS 667977 (c) J.P.Thomas

The Clyndu Level Tramroad, which replaced an earlier wagonway, existed as early as 1761 and provided a direct link between Morris' Clyndu Level Colliery and the Forest copperworks. The tramroad was later joined to the Pentremawled tramroad, which followed the line of Dinas Street to Landore, providing feeder branches to the Rose and Birmingham smelters. The Clyndu tramroad fell out of use around 1790, when a spur line linking the Forest works with the Rose and Birmingham works' tramroads was constructed on the west side of the Swansea Canal. (See Plates 8 & 9)

(Plate 8) Remains of Pentremawled tramway, which ran along Pentremawled Road, Morriston, joining a spur line crossing the Morriston/Swansea trunk road leading to the Swansea Canal and Rose Copperworks. SS 665965. December 2017. (c) J.P.Thomas.

When the tramway, following what is now Clyndu Street, reached the Swansea Turnpike Road, where the 'Duke' public house stands on the right hand corner, its route was confronted by a ridge, which then led to a steep embankment some 77.2 feet above the Tawe valley floor and the canal surface. This topography would have impeded the tramway's construction to follow a direct angled incline to the copperworks.

(Plate 9) Remains of Pentremawled Tramway at Plasmarl which ran along Dinas Street Landore to Morriston. A short connected inclined spur line, shown here, crossed the Swansea to Morriston trunk road leading to the Swansea Canal and Rose Copperworks. SS 665965. December 2017. (c) J.P.Thomas.

(Plate 10) View of Lower Clyndu Street, showing the ridge of level land (now a car sales park) leading to the Morriston/Landore by-pass and former Morriston Branch Copper Pit railway cutting. December 2016. SS 669972 (c) J.P.Thomas

Interestingly, the Morriston History Group stated in their news-letter of April 2017: "There were two Clyndu levels, the up-per 'dry' level and the lower boat level at the foot of the Graig near the present-day Duke's Arms. Both were opened in around 1750 by Lockwood, Morris & Co under their 1746 lease from the duke of Beaufort."

However, as events will unfold, the existence of a "lower boat level" near the Duke's Arms public house was a myth. The en-trance referred to was the tunnel portal of the Clyndu tramway.

If we study an aerial view of Toyota Motors's premises, which are built on the ridge supported by the large GWR stone em-bankment wall (Plate 15), the far right building is oddly con-structed at an angle, seemingly to avoid our suggested route of the tunnel. Moreover, where we believe the tunnel portal was positioned behind the wall, the G.W.R. installed a large cast iron drainage duct which would have carried any water from the tunnel bore under the track embankment and into the ca-nal. The drainage duct remains to this day. (Plate 13) Courtesy National Library of Scotland.

(Plate 11) Likely site of tramway tunnel at GWR retaining wall built to support Morriston Branch Railway cutting embankment at site of Copper Pit Halt Station. December 2016 SS 669972
(c) J.P.Thomas.

(Plate 12) Aerial view of likely site of Clyndu Incline Tunnel Portal at the 'Duke' public house leading to Copper Pit Railway Siding and Forest Copperworks. Interestingly none of Toyota's surface buildings are constructed over the tunnel route. November 2016. SS 669972. Courtesy National Library of Scotland.

We sent our findings to the City and County of Swansea Planning Department and the author was kindly invited to view the 'Toyota' building planning application No. 89/0458/03 dated 6 July 1989.

The report of the Director of Development's planning report states:

"The developer shall submit a detailed site plan of the proposed development indicating the siting of the proposed building and the line of the culvert [old tunnel] traversing the site, the proposed building shall be sited no less than 3 metres from the centre line of the culvert. A detailed scheme relating to this dimension shall be submitted for the consideration of the Director of Development. No works shall commence on site until such details have been agreed in writing with the Director of Development. The diversion works shall form an integral part of the development (i) in order to protect the culvert traversing the site."

This report largely supports Oakley Walters J.P's account of the Clyndu Tramway in 'The Cambrian Daily Leader' 1925, particularly the location of the tunnel:

"Coal was supplied from the old Clyndu Level by an underground canal. The opening of the old canal is to be seen at present on the railway near Copper Pit siding."

However, what Walters observed was the horse drawn wagons from the Clyndu Level entering and leaving the tunnel having delivered their coal to the Forest works.

(Plate 13) View of GWR cast iron water drainage duct at likely site of former Clyndu Tramway Tunnel Entrance. The duct would have taken the drained water under the railway trackbed and into the adjacent canal. SS 669972 November 2016. (c) J.P.Thomas.

Interestingly, when London Merchant Chauncey Townsend sank his Steam Engine Pit at Landore in 1762, he faced a similar obstacle to building a tramway from his colliery to the navigable River Tawe. A map of 1768 shows a shallow tunnel, some 40 yds long, with a tramway linking his colliery to a quay alongside the River Tawe. Townsend's operations were based on Pwll yr Ayr (Golden Pit) which lay to the south-east of today's Brynhyfryd Square. Townsend was granted a lease in 1762 and by 1768 had constructed several wagonways to coaling wharves on the river Tawe. By 1770, Townsend had sunk a shaft at a depth of some 163 yards to reach the Swansea six foot seam. However the operations at Pwll yr Ayr lasted until 1780 when they were abandoned, with the result that the workings flooded. John Morris bought Townsend's pit and tramway in the early nineteenth century and connected it by a branch-line to the head of the Cwm Level incline the quay for shipping his coal.[6]

However, the Clyndu Level Colliery was to experience a new lease of life. In November 1908 the Swansea Waters and Sewers Committee met to discuss a proposal to construct an underground service reservoir above the 'Lan' in the workings of the disused Clyndu Level Colliery. It was said that the surface belonged to Sir Robert Morris, and the minerals under lease from the Duke of Beaufort. Discussion ensued as to the advisability of purchasing the minerals beneath the surface, and as some of it had been worked many years ago, fear was expressed that there might be a subsidence. The Mayor took this view, and said the only alternative was to select another and a Mr Martin thought there was no fear of a subsidence where there was solid ground 100 yards deep. Mr Livingston was in favour of securing the whole of the underlying measures, including the deepest, which would in time become stable. It was mentioned that if the five-foot (Penvilian) seam ore was secured this would obviate any possible subsidence, and it was resolved to negotiate for the site and also for the mine down to and induding the five-foot seam [Penvilian]. The Engineer, in answer to M.T. Hopfeen, stated the cost of the reservoir would be approx. £12,000 and mains approx. £8,000.[7]

Ironically, the surface of the site belonged to Sir John Morris and the minerals, including the Penvilian Coal Vein, under lease from the Duke of Beaufort, so the Committee had to negotiate the securing of all the underlying measures including the coal from the five foot seam.[8] What monies were paid out for securing the underlying coal measures is unknown. (Cambrian 27 November 1908 p.5 Welsh Papers on Line.)

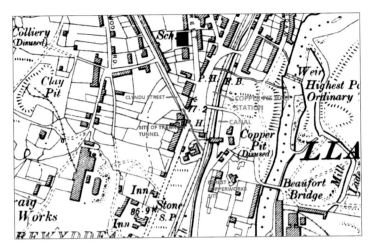

(Plate 14) 1870 O.S. Map of Morriston showing the most likely route of Morris's Clyndu Wagonway to the Forest Copper Works passing under the Swansea turnpike road: based on P.R. Reynold's map of the Clyndu Tramroad. SS 669972 courtesy O.H.M.S.

On 21 April 1909 the Committee agreed to negotiate for the minerals at the Caemawr site close to the former Clyndu Level Colliery; so technically this would be the last occasion that black diamonds were actually mined from the Great Penvilian Vein.

Interestingly, Mr, D.W.A. Saunders, a mining expert,who surveyed the workings of the Clyndu colliery, makes no mention of an underground navigational canal.

Following the construction of the underground service reservoir a Victorian styled control tower was built on the embankment adjacent to Tan-y-lan Terrace, which can be seen in the following photograph:

(Plate 15) Swansea Water and Sewers Committee's announcement on the proposed Morriston Service Reservoir. Evening Express 21 April 1909 p.2 Welsh Papers Online.

(Plate 16) View of Reservoir Control Tower and Access Steps, situated on the bank above Tan-y-lan Terrace which controlled the water flow from an underground service reservoir built by Swansea Corporation in the former workings of the Clyndu Level Colliery. Caemawr can be seen in the distance. SS 665958. (c) J.P.Thomas. April 1960.

With the building of the Caemawr housing estate and modifications to the junction of Trewyddfa Road and Tan-y-lan, the tower and steps have since been demolished and replaced by a smaller but mundane concrete block structure as seen in the following photograph:

(Plate 17) 1930's View of Reservoir Control Tower looking over Morriston. Courtesy Lizzie East.

(Plate 18) Replacement Water Control Tower for Morriston Service Reservoir. SS 665958 in Tanylan Terrace. (c) J.P.Thomas 15 March 2018.

In the next chapter we will look at the Clyndu Water Machine Pit, a design which was commonly used in other coal pits in the Swansea district.

CHAPTER IV
BIBLIOGRAPHY AND ILLUSTRATIONS

(1) Badmington Papers. Letter of November, 1793. National Library of Wales,

(2) 'Copperopolis: Landscapes of the Early Industrial Period In Swansea', S. Hughes, p.p.100, 101. R.C.A.H.M.W. {known as the 'Tirdonkin Fault} (3)'O. Walters J.P., 'Morriston of the 1840's and beyond', Cambrian Daily Leader', 31 July 1925,

(4) P.R. Reynolds, Clyndu and Pentremawled Tramroads, Morriston', South West Wales Industrial Archaeology Society, No.13, July, 1976.

(5) E.T. Svedenstierna, Svedenstierna's Tour of Great Britain 1802-3, David & Charles, 1973, p.43-44.

(6) S. Hughes, Landscapes of the Early Industrial Period In Swansea'p.83 Archaeology Society, No.13, July, 1976.

(7) Cambrian 27 November 1908 p.5

(8) Ibid

(Plate 1) Aerial View of Site of Clyndu Level Colliery Entrance, Uplands Terrace, Morriston. The houses on the left of the entrance are built on the site of the Clyndu Level Colliery pony stables. February 2017 SS 666978. Courtesy National Library of Scotland.

(Plate 2) Site of Entrance to Clyndu Level Colliery (now landscaped) in Uplands Terrace, Morriston. May 2012. The paved path on the right remains a public right of way leading to upper Clyndu Street. SS 666978. The tramway followed Upland Terrace to its junction with Clyndu Street. December 2016. (c) J.P.Thomas.

(Plate 3) Lewis Thomas's 1761 Map of the Fee of Trewydda. Courtesy West Glamorgan Archives (Badmington Collection Vol.72, Plate 27).

(Plate 4) Enlarged Section of Lewis Thomas's 1761 Map of the Fee of Trewydda showing Forest Copperworks and 'straight-line' Clyndu Tramroad. There is no reference to a Clyndu boat level canal nor a navigational canal. Note the large pond fed by the canal which would have supplied water to drive the copperworks' machinery. Courtesy West Glamorgan Archives (Badmington Collection Vol.72, Plate 27).

(Plate 5) Descending coal Waggons using the brake at Bridgewater, Manchester, 1863. Courtesy 'A Nineteenth-Century Colliery Railway', Joyce H.M.Banks,p.161. (Plate 6) P.R. Reynold's 1975 Map of the Routes of the Clyndu Street and Pentremawled Tramroads. Note the straight line of the route to the Forest copperworks which crossed the later Trewyddfa Canal by means of a bridge. Courtesy South West Wales Industrial Archaeology Society.

(Plate 7) View of upper Clyndu Street looking downwards from junction with Uplands Terrace where the Clyndu Level entrance was sited. The junction on the right is Pentremawled Road where a tramroad was later constructed. December 2016 SS 667977 (c) J.P.Thomas.

(Plate 8) Remains of Pentremawled tramway spur line which crossed the Morriston/Swansea trunk road, leading to the Swansea Canal and Rose copperworks. (c) J.P. Thomas. December 2017.

(Plate 9) Remains of Pentremawled tramway which ran along Dinas Street, joining a spur line crossing the Morriston/Swansea trunk road leading to the Swansea Canal and Rose Copperworks. December 2017. (c) J.P.Thomas.

(Plate 10) View of Lower Clyndu Street, showing the ridge of level land (now a car sales park) leading to the Morriston/Landore by-pass and former Morriston Branch Copper Pit Railway Cutting. December 2016. SS 669972 (c) J.P.Thomas.

(Plate 11) Likely site of Tramway Tunnel at GWR retaining wall built to support Morriston Branch Railway cutting embankment at site of Copper Pit Halt Station. December 2016 SS 669972 (c)J.P.Thomas.

(Plate 12) Aerial view of suggested site of Clyndu Incline Tunnel Portal at the 'Duke' public house leading to (Copper Pit Railway Siding) and Forest Copperworks. Interestingly none of F.R.F.'s surface buildings are constructed over the tunnel route. November 2016 SS 669972 Courtesy National Library of Scotland.

(Plate 13) View of GWR Cast Iron Water Drainage Duct at site of former Clyndu Tramway Tunnel Entrance. The duct would have taken the drained water under the railway trackbed and into the adjacent canal. SS 669972 November 2016.(c) J.P.Thomas.

(Plate 14) 1870 O.S. Map of Morriston showing the most likely route of Morris's Clyndu Wagonway to the Forest Copper Works passing under the Swansea turnpike road: based on P.R. Reynold's map of the Clyndu Tramroad. SS 669972 Courtesy O.H.M..S.

(Plate 15) Swansea Water and Sewers Committee's announcement on the proposed Morriston Service Reservoir. 21 April 1909. Courtesy Welsh Papers Online.

(Plate 16) View of Reservoir Control Tower.situated on the bank above Tan-y-lan Terrace, Morriston, which controlled the water flow from an underground service reservoir built by Swansea Corporation in the former workings of the Clyndu Level Colliery. SS 665958. April 1960. (c) J.P.Thomas.

(Plate 17) 1930's View of Reservoir Control Tower, taken from an old Morriston postcard. J.P. Thomas.

(Plate 18) Replacement Control Tower for Morriston Service Reservoir. SS 665958 at Tanylan Terrace. 15 March 2018. (c) J.P.Thomas.

CHAPTER V

THE CLYNDU WATER MACHINE PIT

Coal from the Clyndu Water Machine Pit was destined to a second smelter at the Forest Works built in 1746–48 and had a specially made cart-road that ran diagonally up the hillside to the Pit on the western valley side above the site of what is now Morriston.[1] The Pit was sited to the west of Vicarage Road opposite its junction with Cwm-bath Road. (Plate 1)

(Plate 1) Site of Clyndu Water Machine Pit at junction of Vicarage Road and Cwm Bath Road, Morriston. SS666980. February 2017. Courtesy National Library of Scotland.

A water machine engine of the type illustrated in Plate 2 was commonly used in coal pits in south Wales, and comprised of a bladed vertical wheel mounted on a horizontal axle. The water fed from a leat at speed hits the wheel low down, typically in the bottom quarter, causing the wheel to rotate. The axle was fixed to a capstan shaft for winding and pumping purposes. The water was fed in a large volume at a low head. The efficiency of the machine was about 20% prior to the 18th century and with the later introduction of curved blades this improved to between 50 and 60%. The water hitting the blades was known as the head race and the discharged water as the tail race.

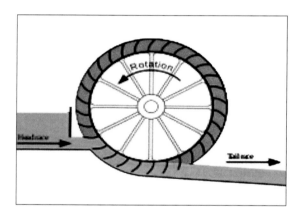

(Plate 2) Diagram of a Water Machine Engine.
Courtesy Researchgate net.

Here the water pump and the winding gear were powered by a water wheel-engine. There were no millponds in the vincinity to provide a fast flowing water leat to operate the machinery, so Lockwood, Morris & Co. constructed a long underground drainage canal from Clase Bach diverting water to the 'Clyndu Water Machine Pit'. The coal workings of this pit had extended its headings northwards towards the Penvilia five feet seam when the Clyndu Level Colliery opened. However, transporting coal to the copperworks by cart-road was both difficult and time consuming, particularly during inclement weather. Even today, during heavy rainfall, brown ironstone contaminated water seeps from the old water machine pit workings and flows down Cwm Bath Road near its junction with Lan Street.

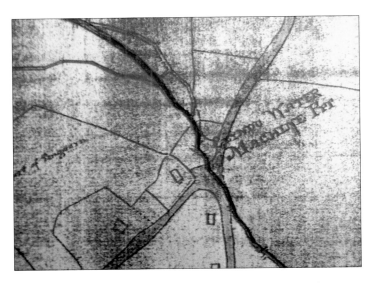

(Plate 3) Enlarged section of 1830 map tracing of the Clyndu Water Machine Pit showing the feeder 'Canal Underground Formally' (blue) joining Morris's Clyndu Level Roadway (red). Courtesy Swansea University Library Richard Burton Archives. Ref: LAC/95/A/1.

(Plate 4) Brown Ironstone contaminated water stains from drain in Lan Street, Morriston. SS 666981. July 2017 (c) J.P.Thomas.

(Plate 5) Brown Ironstone contaminated water leaking from drain in Cwm Bath Road, Morriston. SS 666981. June 2018 (c) J.P.Thomas.

In the next chapter we will look at a little mentioned colliery known as the 'Fire Engine Coalery' situated on a site bordered by Clyndu Street, Harries Street, Morfydd Street and Uplands Terrace, near to where the entrance to the Clyndu Level Colliery was sited. The name 'fire engine' came about as a result of the spread of Newcomen's atmospheric mining pump engines, one of which was sited at the colliery.

CHAPTER V
BIBLIOGRAPHY AND ILLUSTRATIONS

(1) Copperopolis: Landscapes of the Early Industrial Period In Swansea', S. Hughes, p.122, R.C.A.H.M.W. 2000.

(Plate 1) Site of Clyndu Water Machine Pit at junction of Vicarage Road and Cwm Bath Road, Morriston. SS666980. February 2017. Courtesy National Library of Scotland.

(Plate 2) Diagram of a Water Machine Engine. Courtesy Wikipedia.

(Plate 3) Enlarged Section of 1830 map tracing of the Clyndu Water Machine Pit showing the feeder 'Canal Underground Formally' joining Morris's Clyndu Level Roadway. Courtesy Richard Burton Archives. Ref: LAC/95/A/1

(Plate 4) Brown Ironstone contaminated water stains from drain in Lan Street, Morriston. June 2017 SS 666981. (c) J.P.Thomas.

(Plate 5) Brown Ironstone contaminated water stains in Cwm Bath Road, Morriston. June 2018 SS 667981. (c) J.P.Thomas

CHAPTER VI

FIRE ENGINE COALERY (CLYNDU PIT)

There was also a little mentioned colliery known as the 'Fire Engine Coalery' (or colliery) situated on a site bordered by Clyndu Street, Harries Street, Morfydd Street and Uplands Terrace, near to where the entrance to the Clyndu Level Colliery was sited. The name 'fire engine' came about as a result of the spread of Newcomen's atmospheric mining pump engines, one of which was sited at the colliery. These engines had a coal fired furnace to heat the boiler water and by all accounts lit up the night sky.

(Plate 1) Aerial view of 'Fire Engine Colliery' site at Trewydda, abounded by Uplands Terrace, Harries Street, Morfydd Street and Clyndu Street, Morriston. March 2017. SS 667977. Courtesy National Library of Scotland.

The Fire Engine Colliery, often mistakenly referred to as Clyndu Pit, was initially a separate enterprise to the Clyndu Level Colliery and had a Newcomen designed engine house which provided steam power to drive a deep mining pump and operate a capstan shaft some 120 yards deep. Collieries were sometimes referred to as 'Coalieries' where they had a 'central yard' with a blacksmith, saw pit and other mining repair machinery, to which other collieries had access to on payment. The colliery was working the three and two foot seams below the Penvilia Vein and we know from a colliery account that coal was being mined between 1778 to 1779 and sold to the Forest Copperworks (Plate 2). After the Lockwood, Morris & Co. partnership came to an end in 1798, the colliery site and coal seams were re-let to John Morris II in 1803 who thus acquired the Clyndu Engine House and pumping shaft. It is likely that the colliery's capstan shaft linked up the several adits or levels, being worked into the Trewyddfa hillside to the west of Morriston. Hence the enterprises merged and became the 'Clyndu Mine.'

The colliery also had a tramway siding with a connection to the Clyndu wagonway. This can be seen in the 1879 ground plan of the enterprise which shows the Capstan Shaft and Engine House and the trackbed of the former tramway. (Plate 4) This arrangement enabled the coal to be shipped to the Forest works using the wagonway.

It would appear that during the year 1778–1779 coal production at the Clyndu Level must have been insufficient for the smelting furnaces at the Forest works, since coal to the value of £1509. 0. was shipped from the Fire Engine Coalery. (Plate 2)

Coal from the fire Engine Coalery in Trewyddva To y Copperworks of Mess.rs Lockwood, Morris & Co. from Mich.s 1778 to Miches 1779

1778	W.r	Load.s	1779	W.r	Load.s		
October 31.st	104	23	april 24.th	86			
Nov. 28.th	119	17	may - 29.th	106			
Dec.r 26.th	96	39	June - 26.th	149	17		
1779 January 30.th	205	6	July 31.	162	44		
February 27.th	108	6	Aug.t 28.th	133	5		
March 27.th	104	33	Sep.tr 25.th	136	10		
	735	24		773	26	1509	0

*(Plate 2) Account of coal sold from Fire Engine Coalery in
Trewyddva to Forest Copperworks 1778–1779
Courtesy National Library Wales.*

Morris seems to have discontinued its use before the end of his lease in 1845. The 1854 lease to Glasbrook & Richard schedules all the colliery assets that were in place at the various pits on the lease. The entry for Clyndu simply records an engine-house and pit but no engine[1], which suggests that the Newcomen engine had been removed in readiness for a replacement by the more efficient Cornish beam engine. In 1854 Glasbrook & Richard (Glasbrook Brothers Ltd.) Colliery Proprietors acquired the shaft as part of their lease of coal under the fee of Trewyddfa. They installed a Cornish pumping engine with an egg-end boiler and a lift of pumps and used it to pump water from Copper and Forest pits situated on the valley floor. The egg-ended boiler was an early form of tubular wagon boiler with hemispherical ends to support higher steam pressures which enabled the Cornish beam engine to operate more efficiently. (Plate 3)

(Plate 3) Staffordshire Engine House using 'Egg Boiler'. Here the linear motion of the pumpshaft has been converted to rotary motion to operate a shaft winder. Courtesy Lancashire Industrial History Society.

(Plate 4) 1879 Coloured O.S. Map showing site of Fire Engine Coalery (Colliery). Note the the Engine House and site of Capstan Shaft. The track bed of the tramway which joined the Clyndu Level Tramway can also be seen. The Clyndu Level Colliery is shown as closed, while the Engine House and Capstan Shaft of the Fire Engine Colliery must have been operational. SS 667977. Courtesy O.H.M.S.

(Plate 5) View of Fire Engine Coalery site looking westwards towards Morfydd Street. SS 667977 May 2012 (c) J.P.Thomas.

(Plate 6) Site of capped Capstan Shaft, Clyndu Colliery Site. SS 667977 May 2012 (c) J.P.Thomas.

(Plate 7) Remains of Fire Engine Colliery Pump Engine House. Note the large black slag blocks, a bi-product of copper smelting, used as corner stones. SS 667925 May 2012. (c) J.P.Thomas

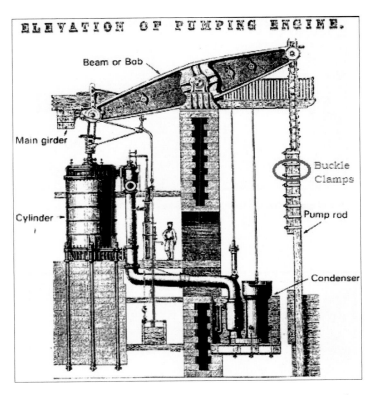

ELEVATION OF PUMPING ENGINE.

Beam or Bob

Main girder

Buckle Clamps

Cylinder

Pump rod

Condenser

(Plate 8) Drawing of a typical Cornish Pumping Engine. Note the pump rod which is clamped to the main beam rod by means of buckle clamps. This arrangement allows the pump rod stroke to be adjusted. Courtesy Trevithick Society.

In the classical arrangement of the Cornish pump, the engine lifts the pump rods and the latter, by virtue of their weight, force the water up on their succeeding down or outdoor stroke. For reasons of strength, the hard wood rods in the shaft have to be made of a great size; in this case they are 20in square at surface, tapering down to 16in square at the bottom of the shaft. The total rod weight, including the connecting iron plates, the poles, etc. is more than twice the weight of the column of water in the shaft. To avoid excessive strain on the rods, and very heavy coal consumption, it is necessary to balance out as much of the excess weight as possible. This was done by having a balance beam or bob on the surface, three more underground working in big chambers cut out of the solid rock, and a water balance near the bottom of the shaft. Note that the hard wooden pump rod is connected to the beam rod with a series of metal buckle clamps shown, one of which the author recovered from the remains of the Fire Engine Coalery engine house (Plate 9).

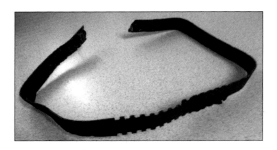

(Plate 9) Remains of metal Pump Shaft Adjustment Buckle Clamp recovered at Site of Clyndu Engine House. 15 May 2015. SS 667977 (c) J.P.Thomas.

(Plate 10) Close-up view of Pump Shaft Buckle Clamp recovered at site of Clyndu Engine House. 15 May 2015. SS 667977 (c) J.P.Thomas.

(Plate 11) 1870 Photograph of Morriston showing Fire Engine House with Pump Beam and Rod. Note the dismantled tramway siding. Also the ornate roof chimney/air vent, normally associated with a Newcomen engine house, has been removed.
SS 667925. Courtesy Morriston History Forum.

(Plate 12) Pre-1870 view of Fire Engine Coalery, Morriston. Note the ornate roof chimney/air vent design, associated with the Newcomen engine, on gable end of engine house. SS 667925 Courtesy Morriston History Forum.

In 1806 Clyndu was one of the levels assigned by Lockwood & Co the Penvilia Vein Company. The new company built a tramroad system to link their levels to the various copperworks on the valley floor that were their principal customers, including a branch from Clyndu which ran down to the Rose copperworks. The upper part of this tramroad survives as Pentremalwed Road. In 1839 all the assets of the Penvilia Vein Co, including Clyndu level, were transferred to the newly formed Swansea Coal Company, backdated to January 1838. By this time Clyndu workings, all in the Five Foot [Penvilian], extended as far as Mynyddbach, Cefngyfelach, Penrhiwfelen and Pentrepoeth. The Notes and Reports on the County Rate [Glamorgan] by the J.E. Bicheno Committee of 1842 reported that Clyndu and the other Penvilia Co. levels were likely to be exhausted within three years. By 1844, once the Swansea Coal Company's new pits at Mynydd Newydd and Pentrefelen were on stream, coal production ceased from the old coal levels, including Clyndu, although it was retained for access to the coal levels.[2]

The 1854 lease to Glasbrook & Richard schedules all the engines that were in place at the various pits on the lease. The entry for Clyndu simply records an engine-house and pit but no engine.[3] In 1854 Glasbrook & Richard acquired the shaft as part of their lease of coal under the fee of Trewyddfa. They installed a Cornish pumping engine with an egg-end boiler and a lift of pumps and used it to pump water from Copper and Forest pits.

However, its use was intermittent and it was only activated when required. Their lease expired in 1896. In 1898 Clyndu pumping engine was subsequently included in the leases to Morriston Collieries Ltd of 1898 and to Copper Pit Collieries Ltd of 1906. The pit is shown as active on the 1899 25 inch OS plan but on the 1917 revision it is shown as disused.[4]

In the 1940s the capstan shaft was probed to a depth of 57 metres with only void space being encountered. There were no shallow mine workings present. Filling of the shaft by the Coal Authority commenced about the same time. It was inferred that the fill had settled to depths in excess of 57 metres, although earlier historical records suggested a shaft depth of 122 metres.

The shaft was capped in the 1950s. Groundwater was found at a depth of 35 metres.

The lower stone courses of the engine house (Plate 7) survived until January 2015 when they were removed as part of work carried out by the Coal Authority to make the site safe for a proposed small housing development, which in the event did not materialise.

The contractors employed by the Coal Authority stated that an old disused and capped mine shaft was located on the development site and had to be dealt with before any building could take place. Geotechnical engineers and geologists, employed by SLS Coastal Surveys, were unable to determine the shape, volume or condition of the mine pumping shaft measuring approximately 24 inches X 24 inches, which the developer requested before it could be backfilled with re-cycled aggregate material.

The contractor broke through the concrete shaft cap and carried out a 3D laser scan survey of the shaft up to the top of the water using the C-ALS (Cavity Auto Laser Scanner) and FARO 3D Focus. In addition, the contractor deployed a multi beam sonar to survey below water level.

(Plate 13) Using the Cavity Auto Laser Scanner in the Fire Engine mine pumping shaft indicated it had a void depth of 67 metres with evidence of a catastrophic failure in parts of the shaft lining. Courtesy SLS Coastal Surveys 2014. SS 667925.

(Plate 14) Computer generated image of scanning data. The blue background is solid ground. The brown background is water. The three terraced houses are situated in Clyndu Street. Courtesy SLS Coastal Surveys 2014. SS 667925.

The survey did not include the capped capstan shaft situated near-by: neither did it reveal any evidence of an underground navigational canal serving the Clyndu Level below the colliery surface.

(Plate 15) Lowering the Cavity Auto Laser Scanner in the Fire Engine mine pumping shaft. Courtesy SLS Coastal Surveys 2014. SS 667925.

However, the South Wales Evening Post, 16th January 2015, carried an article proclaiming that a forgotten Swansea colliery had been uncovered, exposing the pit head of the Clyndu colliery, sparking a hunt for information on the industrial relic.

The author visited the site and identified the circular 'pit head shaft' (Plate 19) as being the throat of the former Cornish Beam Pump engine house, which collected the mine water as it was pumped to the surface. He also investigated the ruins of the demolished pump house and discovered amongst the rubble one of the former adjustable pump shaft steel adjustable buckle clamps (See Plates 9 & 10). The pumping engine house followed the same structure as Scott's engine house in Birchgrove, near Morriston (See Plate 19).

Pumping shafts were usually crammed with heavy equipment and fittings. This equipment needed maintenance, it needed extending, it needed repairing, and that is where a capstan shaft was required. Timber, pumps, pump rods and balance bobs all needed to be lowered and raised in the shaft. It was an important task required to sink the shafts and keep the pumps running. Capstans had a duel purpose and were used for coal haulage as well as servicing heavy pit work located in pumping shafts. As the rope was wound around the drum, it would winch up a cage full of coal while perhaps lowering an empty one. It was the idea of William West, a Cornish engineer, to install a small horizontal engine near the pump shaft, attached to gearing to allow slow control, and use the steam supply from the nearby pumping engine house. It was a simple, obvious use of the steam engine in a new role.

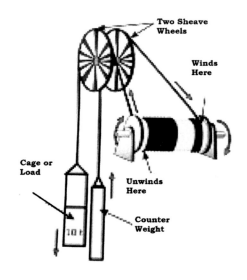

*(Plate 16) The Open Mechanical Engineering Journal,
2018, 12, 95-107 95 1874-155X/18 2018.P*

*(Plate 17) Capstan steam engine with worm gear drive. Courtesy
Navis Book Website.*

(Plate18) Capstan winding drum with worm gear drive.
Courtesy Navis Books Website.

It must have been around 1900, when the Clyndu beam engine house fell out of use, that both the pump rod shaft and the capstan operated pit shaft, which was sited a couple of metres to the north of the engine house, were capped.

In the late 1930s, as part of the World War II effort, the all the metal workings of the surviving pump house beam engine and the capstan shaft machinery were removed for scrap metal. The engine house was then, apart from the ground floor, completely demolished.

(Plate 19) Excavations at the partly demolished Fire Engine House Site revealed the circular 'collar' of the pump shaft which collected the pumped mine water and discharged it through an overflow drain into Morfydd Street, where it flowed downhill to the canal or river Tawe. The pump rod shaft hole measuring about 24 inches X 24 inches was located at the centre of the collar. An example of this arrangement can be seen at the site of Scotts Pit Engine House, Birchgrove, Swansea. SS 667925. (See Plate 20) J.P.Thomas.

(Plate 20) View of Pump Shaft Collar at Scott's Pit Engine House, Birchgrove, Swansea. SS 694 986. Courtesy Scotts Pit Mining Remains.

In the next chapter we will look at the contribution made by Hen Lefel y Graig (Park), Pentrepoeth, Tircanol and Copper Pit collieries in supplying coal to the copper smelters.

CHAPTER VI
BIBLIOGRAPHY AND ILLUSTRATIONS

(1) Second sheet of Deed Parchment with Schedule of Mining Assets contained in John Morris's 1854 Lease to Glasbrook and Richard. Courtesy West Glamorgan Archives Ref: D/D SB 15/56. Details of this lease appear in Chapter XIV

(2) Morriston Library History Group Report. P.16

(3) Second sheet of Deed Parchment with Schedule of Mining Assets contained in John Morris's 1854 Lease to Glasbrook and Richard Courtesy West Glamorgan Archives Ref: D/D SB 15/56 Details of this lease appear in Chapter XIV

(4) O.S. 1899 and O.S. 1917 edition maps 25 inch.

(Plate 1) Aerial View of 'Fire Engine Colliery' site at Trewyddfa, abounded by Uplands Terrace, Harries Street, Morfydd Street and Clyndu Street, Morriston. March 2017. SS 667977. Courtesy maps.nls.uk/os/25inch.

(Plate 2) Account of Coal sold from Fire Engine Coalery in Trewyddfa to Forest Copperworks 1778 – 1779 Courtesy National Library Wales.

(Plate 5) View of Fire Engine Coalery Site looking westwards towards Morfydd Street. SS 667977 May 2012 J.P.Thomas. (Plate 6) Site of capped Capstan Shaft, Clyndu Colliery Site. SS 667977 May 2012 J.P.Thomas.

(Plate 7) Remains of Fire Engine Colliery Pump Engine House. Note the large black slag blocks, a bi–product of copper smelting, used as corner stones. SS 667925 May 2012. J.P.Thomas.

(Plate 8) Drawing of a typical Cornish Pumping Engine. Note the pump rod which is clamped to the main beam rod by means of buckle clamps. This arrangement allows the pump rod stroke to be changed or adjusted. Courtesy Trevithick Society.

(Plate 9) Remains of metal Pump Shaft Adjustment Buckle Clamp found at Site of Clyndu Engine House. 15 May 2015. SS 667977 J.P.Thomas.

(Plate 10) Close-up view of Pump Shaft Steel Buckle Clamp found at site of Clyndu Engine House. 15 May 2015. SS 667977 J.P.Thomas.

(Plate 11) 1870 Photograph of Morriston showing Fire Engine House and Pump Beam and Rod. Note the dismantled tramway siding. Also the ornate roof chimney/air vent, normally associated with a Newcomen engine house, has been removed. SS 667925 Courtesy Morriston History Forum.

(Plate 12) Pre-1870 view of Fire Engine coalery, Morriston. Note the ornate roof chimney/air vent design, associated with the Newcomen engine, on gable end of engine house. SS 667925 Courtesy Morriston History Forum.

(Plate 13) Using the Cavity Auto Laser Scanner in the Fire Engine mine pumping shaft. Courtesy SLS Coastal Surveys 2014. SS 667925.

(Plate 14) Computer generated image of scanning data. The blue background is solid ground. The brown background is water. The three terraced houses are situated in Clyndu Street. Courtesy SLS Coastal Surveys 2014. SS 667925

(Plate 15) Lowering the Cavity Auto Laser Scanner in the Fire Engine mine pumping shaft. Courtesy SLS Coastal Surveys 2014. SS 667925

(Plate 16) Principal operations of a Capstan Operated Shaft. Courtesy The open Mechanical Engineering Journal 2018.

(Plate 17) Capstan steam engine with worm gear drive. Courtesy Navis Book Website.

(Plate 18) Capstan winding drum with worm gear drive. Courtesy Navis Books Website.

(Plate 19) Excavations at the partly demolished Fire Engine House Site revealed the circular 'collar' of the pump shaft which collected the pumped mine water and discharged it through an overflow drain into Morfydd Street, where it flowed downhill to the canal or river Tawe. The pump rod shaft hole measuring about 24 inches X 24 inches was located at the centre of the collar. An example of this arrangement can be seen at the site of Scotts Pit Engine House, Birchgrove, Swansea. SS 667925 Chapter VI, Plate 20. J.P.Thomas.

(Plate 20) View of Pump Shaft Collar at Scott's Pit Engine House, Birchgrove, Swansea. SS 694 986 Courtesy uk mining remains.co.uk

HEN LEFEL Y GRAIG (PARK), PENTREPOETH, TIRCANOL AND COPPER PIT COLLIERIES

Another colliery in the vincinity, supplying coal to the smelters, mainly the Rose copperworks, was the 'Hen Lefel y Graig', which did not open until 1793 when it appeared on a map of Graig Trewyddfa. Its entrance was on an escarpment above Morriston near Trewyddfa Road, 341.1 feet above the valley floor. The coal was brought out using a horse-road or wagonway where it joined the new Pentremawled Tramway which joined the Clyndu Tramway and ran along what is now Dinas Street (Plate 6). In 1894, when John Morris leased his mining assets to Glasbrook and Richard, it was recorded that the colliery had a Pit and Horseway, although the mine was in fact a Level.[1] The colliery ceased production around 1843, but the remains of an tramway or horse-road from the level towards Dinas Street can still be traced.[1]

(Plate 1) Aerial view of site of Hen Lefel y Graig (Park) Colliery. Trewyddfa Road at its junction with Mynydd Garnlwyd Road is on the left of the picture. A tramway or horse-road connected the colliery with the Pentremawled Tramway which followed the route of Dinas Street. SS 665974 February 2017. Courtesy maps.nls.uk/os/25inch.

PENTREPOETH COLLIERY

A little known colliery, with a cart road connection with the Swansea canal, was the 'Pentrepoeth Colliery' situated between Pentrepoeth Road and Springfield Terrace. The site, marked as an 'old colliery and shaft', appears on the 1879 O.S. map of Morriston. We have no information as to the colliery's activities, its opening and eventual closure around 1844.

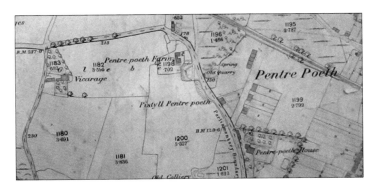

(Plate 2) 1879 O.S. Coloured Map showing site of Pentrepoeth Colliery and Shaft. The Pentrefelen Tramway can also be seen. SS 665974. Courtesy O.H.M.S.

(Plate 3) Aerial view of site of Pentrepoeth Colliery. SS 668983 April 2017. Courtesy maps.nls.uk/os/25inch

It is worth mentioning Tircanol Pit, Morriston, which made use of the Swansea Canal water by getting permission in 1803 to use clean canal water to drive a water machine as long as the mine water was returned to the canal.[2] We have no record of the pit's working history except that for many years the miners at Tircanol pit had a larger underground chapel than Mynydd Newydd pit, but Mynydd Newydd had the distinction of being of being the deepest chapel in the land. Men at the nearby Pentre Pit also assembled for weekly prayers before work. It is thought that they might have met on waste ground nearby.[3]

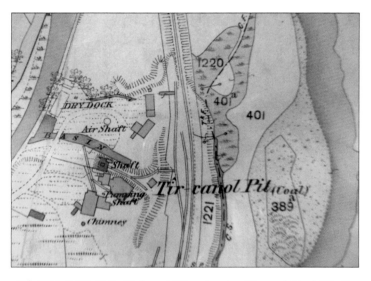

(Plate 4) 1876 O.S. Coloured Map showing Tircanol Coal Pit site. SS 674 986. Courtesy O.H.M.S.

We can see from the site map the pit had a coal loading basin connected to the Swansea Vale Railway and Canal with a dry dock for repairing coal tubs. There was also a tramway connection to the railway with a loading staithe. We have no complete record of the pit's history except that for many years the miners at Tircanol pit had a larger underground chapel than Mynydd Newydd pit.[4] However, it is recorded that on 16 December 1870 John Glasbrook raises 'diamonds' (probably referring to Penvilian coal diamonds) from Tyrcanol Colliery, Morriston. (5) The pit closed in 1875.

There were also three other small un-named pits sunk close to Cwmrhydyceirw as shown on 1870 O.S. Map of Morriston area. We have no record of their working history.

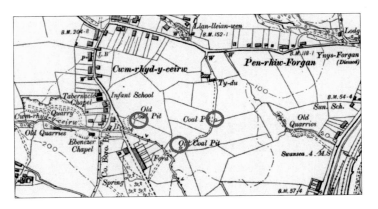

(Plate 5) 1870 O.S. Map showing disused un-named coal pits near Cwmrhydyceirw, Morriston. Courtesy O.H.M.S.

COPPER PIT COLLIERY

The coal mining levels to the west of the river Tawe, e.g. Clyndu and Lefel y Graig, could easily reach the Penvilia Vein's five foot seam, but in order to reach the Swansea Six Foot, Three Foot and Two Foot seams, deep shafts would be required. When Chauncey Townsend sunk the Pwll Mawr in 1770 to reach the Swansea Six Foot seam it was at a depth of 163 yards.[6]

Sometime prior to 1860, a coal mine was first opened on the Copper Pit site by Cory, Yeo and Co. to serve the nearby

Forest copper works with fuel. It originally consisted of a single shaft around 150 yards deep to the Swansea Two Foot Seam. The company had, for some time, established business links with John Glasbrook's Graigola Merthyr Coal Company and by 1885, Glasbrook had taken over the control of Cory, Yeo and Co.

However, in November 1860, John Glasbrook and his co-partner and brother-in-law, Philip Richard, trading as colliery proprietors Glasbrook Brothers Limited struck the Five Foot Penvilia seam at the Copper Pit Colliery site after three years work at a cost of £14,000. The proprietors celebrated their success by giving a substantial dinner to 250 workmen, which was followed by the holding of a special tea for 150 wives of the workpeople. The celebratory dinner, which followed all deep sinkings, was according to the Cambrian's report, was a "crack affair, the champagne flowing about like water." It was the turn of the artisans to be entertained, after which congratulatory addresses were read in English as well as Welsh. The English speech was read by a Mr. H. John, wheel-wright, and the Welsh address by Mr. J. Rees Davies, fitter. The eatables consumed were: 300lbs of beef, 12 hams, 13 legs of pork, 20 geese and a large quantity of plum pudding.[7]

The 'Welshness' of this event may well have had its roots in John Glasbrook's upbringing. He was born in 1816, the son of Thomas and Margaret Glasbrook of Llwyn-y-domen Farm in the parish of Llangyfelach (near Rhydypandy), about a mile and a half to the west of Clydach and baptised on 30 August in that year at Llangyfelach church.

When Phillip Richard died in 1878, John Glasbrook took over Morriston Collieries. He had also purchased Brynmor House in Swansea in 1850, and acquired land on both sides of the Glamorgan/Carmarthenshire border, including farms in the parishes of Llangyfelach, Llandeilo Talybont, Loughor, Swansea, Llandybie and Llanelli. By 1867 he had leased 800 acres of coal bearing land in and around the Cwmdulais valley, near Pontarddulais, and had a railway line built to connect it with the Llanelly and Swansea Extension Railway thus gaining access to both Swansea and Llanelly harbours.

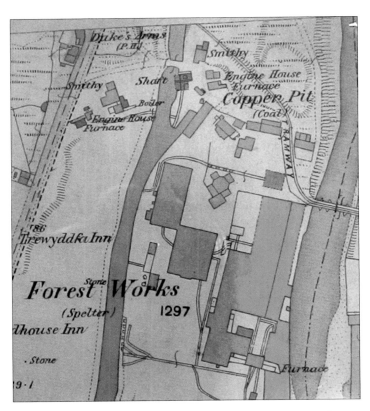

(Plate 6) 1879 coloured O.S. Map showing Copper Pit Colliery on the Forest Copperworks Site which had become a Spelter Works. Note the canal wharves and dock for unloading coal and shipping zinc. There is also a tramroad across the Beaufort Bridge linking the two workssites SS 670972. Courtesy O.H.M.S.

(Plate 7) The former Beaufort Bridge known as 'Hen Bont' or old bridge, designed by William Edwards, was a vital link with industries on both the east and west banks of the river Tawe, particularly John Morris's two works. It also carried a tramway connection. The bridge was demolished in 1968 and replaced with a steel foot-bridge. SS670922 Courtesy Morriston History Group.

(Plate 8) Views of the surviving Copper Pit Engine House, Beaufort Road, Morriston. Note the high arched entrance to facilitate the installation and removal of heavy machinery.
SS670922. April 2017 (c) J.P.Thomas.

125

*(Plate 9) Aerial view of site of Copper Pit Colliery. March 2017.
The new steel-framed Beaufort Bridge crossing the
river Tawe can be seen at bottom right. SS 670972.
Courtesy Nationa Library of Scotland.*

By 1873, John Glasbrook became the owner and took over
the Morriston Collieries Limited in 1878. In 1888 it was listed
with Cwm Pit, Brynhyfryd, both together employing 330 men.
Apparently it was the first colliery in the district to have electrical
powered haulage and winding gear installed. The South Wales
Evening Post reported on 15 April 1893 that a most serious accident happened at Messrs. G. Glasbrook's Morriston Colliery
this morning which almost proved fatal for one of its workers.
Interestingly, in 1854 when John Morris leased his mining assets to Glasbrook and Richard it was recorded:

"AT COPPER PIT One 14 inch high pressure Steam Engine
complete except the brass fittings and sweep rods. Two Boilers
and fittings complete. Pumping apparatus and a lift of 8 inches.
Pumps complete. Pit Top complete."[8]

Morriston Collieries was dissolved in 1898, and Copper pit
was shown on the 1899 OS map as disused. [9]

126

(Plate 10) John Glasbrook (1816–1887) Colliery Owner –
Contemporary Portraits, Men & Women of South Wales &
Monmouthshire, (Western Mail, 1897)

The colliery later came under the ownership of Copper Pit Collieries Ltd., Morriston, Swansea, who re-opened it with the addition of another shaft and by 1908 employed 106 men underground and 19 on the surface, managed by D.L.Thomas.[10]

In 1908 the Copper Pit Brickworks was established on the site. The works is listed in Kelly's 1923 & 26 editions. The works was fortunate to have beds of clay associated with each coal seam and the owners made good use of the fireclay brought out of the mine for the production of bricks. Moreover, there was an ample supply of clay nearby on the slopes of Plasmarl common near Morriston, where the Graig Brick Works, which opened in 1890, established a large clay pit.

(Plate 11) Product from the Copper Pit Brickworks.
Courtesy Martyn Fretwell.

(Plate 12) Product from the Graig Morriston Brickworks.
April 2018 J.P.Thomas.

The total workforce numbered 310 in 1913 and was still managed by D. L. Thomas.

During 1918 there were 357 men working underground and 89 on the surface. The manager at this time was J.Stanbridge.[11]

From the 1923 list there were 333 underground and 75 on the surface with manager J. Morgan, producing 100,000 tons of steam coal from the Two Foot and Three Foot seams. It employed 395 men in 1923 when managed by John Morgan.[12]

However on 1 May 1930, the owners of Copper Pit Colliery announced in the local press its intention to close the colliery:

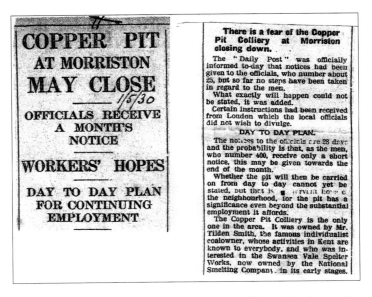

COPPER PIT
AT MORRISTON
MAY CLOSE
_1/5/30_

OFFICIALS RECEIVE
A MONTH'S
NOTICE

WORKERS' HOPES

DAY TO DAY PLAN
FOR CONTINUING
EMPLOYMENT

There is a fear of the Copper Pit Colliery at Morriston closing down.

The "Daily Post" was officially informed to-day that notices had been given to the officials, who number about 25, but so far no steps have been taken in regard to the men.

What exactly will happen could not be stated, it was added.

Certain instructions had been received from London which the local officials did not wish to divulge.

DAY TO DAY PLAN.

The notices to the officials are 28 days and the probability is that, as the men, who number 400, receive only a short notice, this may be given towards the end of the month.

Whether the pit will then be carried on from day to day cannot yet be stated, but that is a vital hope of the neighbourhood, for the pit has a significance even beyond the substantial employment it affords.

The Copper Pit Colliery is the only one in the area. It was owned by Mr. Tilden Smith, the famous individualist coalowner, whose activities in Kent are known to everybody, and who was interested in the Swansea Vale Spelter Works, now owned by the National Smelting Company, in its early stages.

(Plate 13) Intended closure of Copper Pit Colliery, Morriston, 1'
May 1930. Courtesy South Wales Evening Post.

The colliery lingered on a day-to-day existence until it finally closed in 1933 joining the fate of other collieries in this area which was largely due to the prohibitive cost of working the lower seams, the cost of pumping out mine-water, the loss of foreign markets and the general economic conditions and trade depression.[13]

Although John Glasbrook was respected as a good employer by his workforce, he had his reservations about improving their education. He opposed the opening of a public library in Swansea when he wrote in 1870:

"The working classes have too much knowledge already; it was much easier to manage them twenty years ago; the more education people get, the more difficult they are to manage."[14]

John Glasbrook was also instrumental in developing collieries to the west of Swansea at Cwm Burlais in search of the Penvilian biuminous coal which is discussed later. In the following Chapter we will take a close look at the main collieries in the Landore district, which worked the Penvilain seam and supplied bituminous coal to the developing copper smelting industries. These were the Plasmarl and Tir Glandwr which generally worked the lower seams.

CHAPTER VII
BIBLIOGRAPHY AND ILLUSTRATIONS

(1) Second sheet of Deed Parchment with Schedule of Mining Assets contained in John Morris' 1854 Lease to Glasbrook and Richard Courtesy West Glamorgan Archives Ref: D/D SB 15/56 Details of this lease appear in Chapter XIV.

(2) Copperopolis. Landscapes of the Early Industrial Period in Swansea. S. Hughes. RCAHMW, 2000, p.111

(3) 'Treboeth Historical & Pictorial Record'.Treboeth Historical Society, 2012. p.118.

(4) Copperopolis. Landscapes of the Early Industrial Period in Swansea. S. Hughes. RCAHMW, 2000, p.118

(5) Fforestfach History

(6) Copperopolis. Landscapes of the Early Industrial Period in Swansea. S. Hughes. RCAHMW, 2000, p.108

(7) The Story of Swansea's Districts and Villages' N.L. Thomas, Parts 1-3 Guardian Press, 1959, p.147

(8) Indentured Lease Agreement Parchment First Sheet from Duke of Beaufort to Phillip Richard and John Glasbrook dated 2 October 1854.

(9) Welsh Coal Mines Forum (un-numbered document)

(10) Ibid

(11) Ibid

(12) Ibid

(13)

(14) Swansea an Illustrated History, Glanmor Williams, 1990, C. Davies, p.167

(Plate 6) 1879 coloured O.S. Map showing Copper Pit Colliery on the Forest Copperworks Site which had become a Spelter Works. Note the canal wharves and dock for unloading coal and shipping zinc. There is also a tramroad across the Beaufort Bridge linking the two Forest workssites SS 670972. Courtesy O.H.M.S.

(Plate 7) The former Beaufort Bridge known as 'Hen Bont' or old bridge, designed by William Edwards, was a vital link with industries on both the east and west banks of the river Tawe, particularly John Morris's two works. It also carried a tramway connection. The bridge was demolished in 1968 and replaced with a steel footbridge. SS670922 Courtesy Morriston History Forum

(Plate 8) Views of the surviving Copper Pit Engine House, Beaufort Road, Morriston. Note the high arched entrance to facilitate the installation and removal of heavy machinery. SS670922. April 2017 (c) J.P.Thomas.

(Plate 9) Aerial view of site of Copper Pit Colliery. March 2017. The new steel-framed Beaufort Bridge crossing the river Tawe can be seen at bottom right. SS 670972 Courtesy National Library of Scotland.

(Plate 10) John Glasbrook (1816–1887) Colliery Owner – Contemporary Portraits, Men & Women of South Wales & Monmouthshire, (*Western Mail*, 1897)

(Plate 11) Product from the Copper Pit Brickworks. Courtesy M. Fretwell.

(Plate 12) Product from the Graig Morriston Brickworks. April 2018 (c) J.P.Thomas

(Plate 13) Intended Closure of Copper Pit Colliery, Morriston, 1' May 1930. Courtesy South Wales Evening Post

CHAPTER VIII

PLASMARL AND LANDORE PITS

By the mid-1760s Morris was starting to work the deeper 6 Foot Vein from the valley floor. Plas-marl Pit was opened around 1765 followed by Landore in around 1770. These were all served by wagonways as opposed to coal roads.

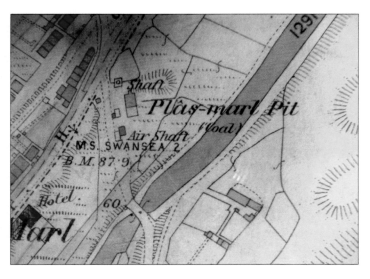

(Plate 1) 1881 coloured O.S. Map showing site of Plasmarl Coal Pit alongside the Swansea Canal. SS 665 964. Courtesy O.H.M.S.

Output was primarily intended for the export market and so the wagonways focused on the New Quay at Landore.[1] However, we have no record of the output of these levels, nor their closure. Neither do we have any record of the route taken by Morris,

Lockwood & Co.'s new wagonway constructed in 1769–71 to transport coal from their Plas-y-Marl Level, across the Swansea Canal to a quay on the river Tawe at Landore, although a canal bridge shown at the site of the level, led to Siemens Steel Works via. a swing bridge across the river Tawe.

A long feeder was built from the Nant Rhyd-y-filais to a new reservoir at Plasmarl to bring water to the water wheel winder at this pit probably in 1775. In 1785 a Boulton and Watt steam winder replaced it fed by a local source. The Plasmarl pit was completely converted to steam power by 1801.

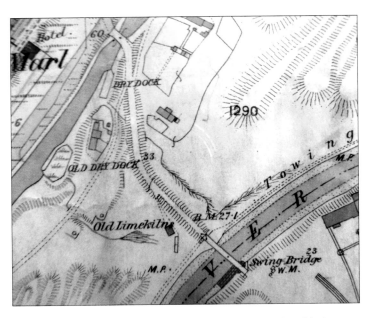

(Plate 2) 1881 coloured O.S. Map showing route of road link connecting Neath Road and Plasmarl Pit with Siemens Steel works. Note the Swing Bridge over the river Tawe and the Dry Dock for repairing the coal barges. It is probable that Morris used this route for his earlier waggonway to the navigable river. Note the river Tawe towing path, which suggests that larger vessels were towed to their berths. SS 665 964 Courtesy O.H.M.S.

(Plate 3) View downstream at a swing-bridge providing vehicular access from the Neath Road and Plasmarl Pit across the river Tawe to the Siemens Steelworks. Morris's waggonway may have used this route to reach the navigable river. The pipeline strapped to the bridge structure probably conveyed water from the Swansea Canal to the Siemens Steelworks for their steam-engines powering rolliing mills and blast machinery. The bridge, opened in 1871, was more than likely out of use when the photograph was taken, since the pipline would have interrupted its operation.
SS 665962. Courtesy West Glamorgan Archives – GWR Collection.

(Plate 4) Remains of the swing bridge support piers December 2017. SS 665962 (c) J.P.Thomas.

(Plate 5) Remains of the swing bridge turntable pier and rails December 2017 SS 665962 (c) J.P.Thomas.

(Plate 6) 1881 coloured O.S. Site Map of Tir Glandwr (Landore) Coal Pit (crossed by the G.W.R. Viaduct) which had access to the Swansea Canal and the river Tawe. SS 659950 Courtesy O.H.M.S.

Tir Glandwr (later Drew's) Pit Railway. This was built by Chauncey Townsend between 1768 and 1770 to serve the Tir Glandwr Railway Coal Coal Banks.The railway was still in operation in 1827 but had probably closed by 1838.[2]

A slight quay carried the south arm of the Tir Landore Pit Railway and may have well occupies a small northern piece of what was William Thomas' wharf. The site was empty by 1838. However in 1854, when John Morris leased the Pit's mining assets to Glasbrook and Richard, a substantial piece of machinery was obtained:[3]

"AT LANDORE COAL PIT 14 inch Condensing Engine and Boiler complete."

(Plate 7) The top of the Drew's or Tir Glandwr Pit being cleared of surrounding earthwork to enable filling and fitting with a lower-level cap in preparation for the new cross-valley link road in February 1999. SS 659950 Courtesy West Glamorgan County Council Engineers Department.

(Plate 8) Remains of Canal Bridge at site of Plasmarl Coal Pit. The inclined bridge had been re-inforced to take heavy road traffic to the Landore Steel Works. C. 1959 SS 659950 Courtesy Swansea Docks Collection.

The remains of Chauncey Townsend's tramway tunnel portal leading to the Landore quay can be seen in an old photograph showing the Landore industrial landscape and the Llangyfelach copperworks.

(Plate 9) Picture of derelict Llangyfelach copper works and remains of tramroad tunnel entrance (right of St. John's Church) to the quay on the river Tawe. The Swansea Canal and GWR line to Morriston are in situate so the year the picture was taken is probably around 1920. SS 661959 Courtesy Welsh Coal Mines Forum.

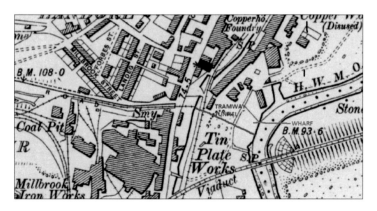

(Plate 10) 1870 O.S. Map of Landore showing the route of Townsend's Tramway and Tunnel to the quay at the river Tawe. When the Swansea Canal wharf opened the tramway was truncated and the tunnel abandoned. SS 654994 Courtesy O.H.M.S.

(Plate 11) View of the derelict Llangyfelach Copperworks and Landore New Quay looking north towards towards Railway Viaduct in early 20th Century. SS 662958. Courtesy British Transport Board. The tunnel area has since been landscaped.

In Shropshire during this period it was common practice for coal to be brought down the sides of the valley to the River Severn, the wagonway running in a continuous line from the coal face to the shipping place. Robert Morris came from Shropshire and was up-to-date industrial methods. In view of this it would be surprising if he did not initially lay down a wooden waggon way, with the rails later being lined with a metal strip.[4] The rails would have reduced friction on the wheels, thus allowing horse-drawn waggons to move along more easily. Another benefit was that horses could now pull loads of up to 13 tonnes, a four fold increase on previously.

The early wagons had 4 wooden wheels 1 foot in diameter, But these were replaced by ones made of iron and in 1729 the Coalbrookdale Ironworks began to produce iron wheels, with an inside flange to run on the rails. The waggons at this time were 10ft long and 4ft wide, pulled by 3 horses and carrying 2½ tons. The extra weight led to the wooden rails, even with a metal strip on top, starting to break because of the weight and hardness of the wheels, which were about 3 hundred weight each.

The next development was to replace the wooden rails with tramplates made completely of iron and by 1768, and to replace the wooden sleepers with stone blocks, which were sturdier, to enable them to be fixed to the sleepers at a gauge of 36 inches. The other type was only 3ft long and 2 inches wide. This type of rail was known as "edge rail" and relied on the flange being on the wagon wheel.

The Morris MS gives details concerning the introduction of Cast Iron Tram Plates – "in Nov'r 1776, I wrote to Messrs Darby and Co, at Coal Brook Dale that I had sent them a pattern in wood about 4 ft long and 5 in wide, to cast Iron plates for wheeling Coal in my Collieries, each plate to weigh about 56 lbs: and if they could be supplied at £8 per ton, I should want about 100 tons, and that the introduction of them would occasion a vast consumption of metal never before used for such a purpose." Twelve years later, in 1778, we learn that there were about 240 tons of Cast Iron Tram Plates underground at the Lockwood & Morris Co.s Pentre, Landore colliery.[5]

However an account given by E.D.Clarke, who visited the Cwm Level pit in 1771 where he was taken underground, described the tramplates as "some sort of a flat plate with a groove down the middle to guide the wagon wheels" – something completely different to tramplates or edge rails. However, with the abundance of debris in mining operations, a groove would soon fill-up causing wagon wheels to derail.[6]

Considering the Clyndu Level was in operation until its closure in 1844, Robert Morris would have almost certainly modernised the Clyndu tramway as he did at his Pentre, Landore colliery when in 1776 when he built some 3 miles of cast iron edge rails into the headings to bring out the coal for shipping. However, the clanking noise and vibration produced by these cast iron tramways caused local people to object to their use on the grounds that noise would be a serious nuisance and that the vibration would surely sour the beer in their cellars.[7]

As was the case with most colliery tramways, it was necessary to have a set of rules for the use of the track to ensure its smooth running, especially as for much of the route, as was the case with the Clyndu Level, there was probably just a single track with passing loops.[8]

- Wagons should have no less than 4 wheels.
- Loaded trams were not to weigh more than 2 tons unless the load was in one piece.
- (Later, stronger tracks meant that heavier loads could be carried).
- Speed was not to exceed 4 miles per hour.
- When loaded and empty 'trains' (or to use the correct term 'gangs') met, the loaded one had priority. When both were loaded (or both unloaded) the first to reach the passing post had priority.
- Travelling was not allowed at night or on Sundays or public holidays.
- No driver was to block the tramroad for more than fifteen minutes. In the case of a breakdown, if a faulty tram could not be repaired in that time it had to be removed from the track.[8]

These tramway operational rules applied generally across South Wales.

In 1793 Morris, Lockwood & Co. moved their copper smelting operations from the Forest site back to Landore, and the Forest works taken over by Harford & Co's brass wire works. In 1809 John Morris withdrew from the company, which became simply Lockwood & Co., and in 1806, on his own behalf, he bought a third share in the collieries owned by that firm. He then formed a new company, known as the Penvilia Vein Co., to exploit the collieries at Penfilia, Treboeth and Clyndu.[9]

As a result of these developments the original purpose of the Clyndu Level Wagonway/Tramroad no longer applied. The interest of the new owners of the level was to sell the coal by way of trade, and it was therefore necessary for them to get it to the newly opened Swansea Canal, using the best available means of transport.

The Clyndu Waggonway/Tramroad fell out of use as such, becoming just an ordinary road, and its function was taken by a new tramroad alignment a little to the west which is now Pentremawled Road. This new tramroad brought coal from Clyndu Level and Hen Lefel y Graig, a little higher up, to a wharf on the canal. Here it was joined by another tramroad from the south-west which ran along which is now Dinas Street, by which coal was transported from other collieries mining the Penvilia Vein. The two branches joined on the western bank of the canal opposite the Rose Copperworks and crossed the canal by a bridge to deliver coal to the copperworks and, possibly, to the Beaufort Dock for shipping on the river.[10] Strategically, the Pentremawled Tramway linked the Clyndu and Hen Level y Graig coal levels with those at Landore owned by Lockwood & Co and Morris, and in turn with their customers, the Rose, Birmingham and Forest works. Following John Morris' lease of the mining assets of the Fee of Trewyddfa to Phillip Richard and John John Glasbrook in 1854, the Clyndu Level became the property of a dynasty of Swansea coal owners whose principal seat of operations was subsequently in the Fforestfach area.[11] The level was closed in 1841 by which this time its workings extended underground as far as Morriston Cemetery. However, in 1868 when Arthur Pendarves Vivian visited Cwm Level Pit, Landore, which was also working the 5 foot Penvilia seam, he reported:

"This ground is all full of old workings and there are no less than 5 levels driven in this neighbourhood in this vein [Penvilian] of which one is Clyndu. They are in fact in this level only scraping out the leavings of the old people." [12]

I would also appear that John Morris ws reluctant to pay for his use of tramroads to convey his coal. The Badmington Papers II No. 2,132 dated 1842 LIST the following statement:

"Notice of action to be taken against Sir John Morris, bart, with regard to payment for the use of tramroads to convey coal from Pentre Pit, Landore Pit, and Plasymarl to Landore Coal Bank, the canal, and Landore Copper Works."

So it seems coal mining at the Clyndu Level lingered on until as late as 1868, providing scrapings (Culm) for the local inhabitants. However, with the cessation of large scale coal production, the Pentremawled Tramroad was abandoned, and, like the Clyndu Waggonway/Tramroad, it became an ordinary road. The tramroad to Penfilia along Dinas Street was still in existence in about 1856, but by 1876 it too had been abandoned.[13]

By 1844, once the Swansea Coal Company's new pits at Mynydd Newydd and Pentrefelen were on stream, coal production ceased from the old coal levels including Clyndu, except for access. The 1746 lease from the Duke of Beaufort, under which the Swansea Coal Co operated, expired in 1845. The company was immediately granted a new lease of the Four and Five Foot veins, including Clyndu. The coal had largely been worked out but the Clyndu levels in the Five Foot were still of value for access to the company's other mineral properties and for drainage and ventilation. On the dissolution of the Swansea Coal Company in 1863 [discussed later] the lease passed to Vivian & Sons. It expired in 1866, no attempt was made to renew it and the Clyndu level was closed.[14] Although, when Arthur Pengreaves Vivian visited collieries on Graig Trewyddfa in 1868, he reported mining activities at the level:

"This ground is all full of old workings and there are no less than 5 levels driven in this neighbourhood in this vein of which this is one – Clyndu. They are in fact in this level only scraping out the leavings of the old people."[15]

In the next chapter we will discuss the opening of the Swansea Canal which was a major development for the coal industry in the lower Swansea valley by greatly improving the bulk transportation of coal from the mines to the copper smelters and processed copper to the Port of Swansea for export.

CHAPTER VIII
BIBLIOGRAPHY AND ILLUSTRATIONS

(1) Copperopolis. Landscapes of the Early Industrial Period in Swansea. S. Hughes. RCAHMW, 2000, p.111

(2) Ibid

(3) John Morris's lease of mining assets to Glasbrook and Richard 1854. Second sheet of Deed Parchment with Schedule of Mining Assets West GlamorganArchive Service ef. No. D/D SB 15/56 Details of this lease appear in Chapter XIV

(4) P.R. Reynolds, Clyndu and Pentremawled Tramroads, Morriston', South West Wales Industrial Archaeology Society, No.13, July, 1976.(un-numbered page)

(5) W. Gerwyn Thomas B.Sc, Ph.d etc., 'The Coal Mining Industry in West Glamorgan' The Glamorgan Historian Vol 6 ed. Steven Williams (pub'd. 1969)

(6) E.D. Clarke during his tour through the South of England and Wales and Part of Ireland. 1793. P.23. Minerva Press.

(7) Alderman Edward Harris *'Swansea, its Port and Trade and their Development'* 1935, Western Mail & Echo Ltd.

(8) Caerleon Net. Operation of the Caerleon Tramway 1834. (un-numbered page)

(9) P.R. Reynolds, Clyndu and Pentremawled Tramroads, Morriston' (un-numbered page)

!10) Ibid.

(11) Ibid

(12) Welsh Journals on Line, Gower, Vol 24 1973, 'The Vivian Collieries in 1868 F. G. Cowley, p.80

(13) ' P.R. Reynolds, Clyndu and Pentremawled Tramroads, Morriston', (un-numbered page)

(14) Morriston History Group. 'Historical Account of the Clyndu Level Colliery, Morriston. 2015. (un-nembered page)

(15) Welsh Journals on Line, Gower, Vol 24 1973,'The Vivian Collieries in 1868 F. G. Cowley, p.80

(Plate 1) 1876 O.S. Map showing site of Plasmarl Coal Pit alongside the Swansea Canal. SS 665 964 Courtesy O.H.M.S

(Plate 2) 1876 O.S. Map showing route of road link connecting Neath Road and Plasmarl Pit with Siemens Steel works. Note the Swing Bridge over the river Tawe and the Dry Dock for repairing the coal barges. It is probable that Morris used this route for his waggonway to the navigable river. SS 665 964 Courtesy O.H.M.S.

(Plate 3) View downstream at a swing-bridge providing vehicular access from the Neath Road and Plasmarl Pit actoss the river Tawe to the Siemens Steelworks. Morris's waggonway may have used this route to reach the navigable river. The pipeline strapped to the bridge structure probably conveyed water from the Swansea Canal to the Siemens Steelworks for their steam-engines powering rolliing mills and blast machinery. The bridge, opened in 1871, was more than likely out of use when the photograph was taken, since the pipline would have interrupted its operation. SS 665962 Courtesy West Glamorgan Archives – GWR Collection.

(Plate 4) Remains of the swing bridge support piers December 2017. SS 665962 (c) J.P.Thomas

(Plate 5) Remains of the swing bridge turntable pier and rails December 2017 SS 665962 (c) J.P.Thomas.

(Plate 6) O.S. 1876 Site Map of Tir Glandwr (Landore) Coal Pit (crossed by the G.W.R. Viaduct) which had access to the Swansea Canal and the river Tawe. SS 659950 Courtesy O.H.M.S.

(Plate 7) The top of the Drew's or Tir Glandwr Pit being cleared of surrounding earthwork to enable filling and fitting with a lower-level cap in preparation for the new cross-valley link road in February 1999. SS 659950 Courtesy West Glamorgan county Council Engineers Department. (S. Hughes. Copperopolis p.314)

(Plate 8) Remains of Canal Bridge at site of Plasmarl Coal Pit. The inclined bridge had been re-inforced to take heavy road traffic to the Landore Steel Works. C.1959 SS 659950 Courtesy Swansea Docks Collection

(Plate 9) Picture of derelict Llangyfelach copper works and remains of tramroad tunnel entrance (right of St. John's Church) to the quay on the river Tawe. The Swansea Canal and GWR line to Morriston are in situate so the year the picture was taken is probably around 1920. SS 661959 Courtesy Welsh Coal Mines Forum.

(Plate 10) 1870 O.S. Map of Landore showing the route of Townsend's Tramway to the quay at the river Tawe. SS 654994 Courtesy O.H.M.S.

(Plate 11) View of the derelict Llangyfelach Copperworks and Landore New Quay looking north towards to-wards Railway Viaduct in early 20th Century. SS 662958 Courtesy British Transport Board. The tunnel area has since been landscaped. (S. Hughes. Copperopolis p.317)

CHAPTER IX

TREWYDDFA AND SWANSEA CANAL

The growth of the metal smelting industries in the lower Swansea Valley on the wesstern banks of the river Tawe, also led to an increased demand for smokeless bituminous coal particularly for the copper, brass and lead smelting works situated on the west bank and a means of exporting their products. These works were:

- Landore, in Llangyfelach parish, built by Dr Lane of Bristol in 1717 and taken over by Morris Lockwood & Co in 1726.
- The Old Copper Works [at the Burlais brook junction with the Tawe], built by James Griffiths.
- Forest, pre 1747, built by Morris Lockwood & Co.
- Birmingham, in 1791, built by Birmingham Mining and Copper Co.
- Rose, in 1795, built by a Birmingham Company.

At the time collieries were linked directly to the smelting works by private tramroads which provided little flexibility for the shipping of refined copper for export or for transporting bulk coal to the refiners.

With the development of Swansea harbour from the 1760s, consideration was given as to how the rich mineral resources of the Tawe Valley could be moved in bulk to the coast. In 1790, William Padley surveyed the valley for a possible canal route, and in 1791, an Act of Parliament to authorise the nearby Neath Canal resulted in calls for a public meeting. A meeting held on 5 April 1793 appointed the canal engineer Thomas Sheasby to conduct a survey.

The plans were opposed by the Duke of Beaufort and other traders, who wanted the canal to terminate further up the river near Landore and Morriston, where they already had wharfs.

Swansea Corporation favoured the route into Swansea, and offered to contribute towards its cost, whereupon the Duke, his son the Marquess of Worcester and the Duke's agent withdrew their subscriptions. This action stirred others to subscribe and £52,000 was raised almost immediately.

Ultimately, a compromise was reached, with the canal terminating in Swansea, but the Duke constructing 1.4 miles (2.3 km) of canal from Nant Rhydyfiliast [Landore] to Nant Felin [Morriston], on which he was allowed to charge tolls, which could not exceed the tolls charged by the canal company for use of the rest of the canal. The Duke's section, which was part of the main line, was called the Trewyddfa Canal and followed the line of Morris' canal built about 1790, measuring just over a mile in length, and ran parallel to the river from the coal banks at Landore up to the Fforest Copper Works below Morriston. It was described in 1793 as belonging to Messrs. Lockwood and Cotton, Lord Eliot and John Morris.[1]

An Act of Parliament authorising the construction was passed on 23 May 1794, and the Swansea Canal Company were empowered to raise £60,000 by issuing shares, and a further £30,000 if required. The Trewyddfa Canal measured 4 feet wide at the bottom & 8 feet wide at top & 4 feet deep[2], and basically resembled a ditch. Nevertheless, the canal provided an economic means of transporting coal in horse drawn trains of tubs or barges to the smelting works in the lower Swansea valley and for shipping refined metals to Swansea Docks for export.

CLYDACH-ON-TAWE DOCKYARD

(Plate 1) Coal tubs and barges moored on the canal at Clydach-on-Tawe dockyard. SS 684005. Courtesy John Hutchings.

Another development which brought traffic to the canal was the opening of The Oystermouth Railway & Tramroad Company, which was authorised by Parliament in June 1804, with Sir John Morris (1775–1855) as its chairman and his son John Armine Morris (1813–93) on the board. The Oystermouth Railway was constructed as a tramway to transport bituminous coal from the Clyne Valley and limestone (smelting flux) from the Dunnes in Mumbles, to the Swansea Canal at Pottery Wharf, where it was shipped to the copper smelters in the western lower Swansea valley.

The rails, laid to a gauge of 1.219m (4ft), were L-shaped tramplates mounted on stone blocks. Edward Martin (c.1763–1818), engineer and owner of Gwaunclawdd Colliery in Powys, carried out surveys and estimates for the work, and oversaw its construction.

*(Plate 2) Horse-drawn barge on Swansea Canal at Vivian's
Copperworks, Hafod. C1860. SS 660951.
Courtesy Swansea Museum Collection.*

By 1799, as much as 250 tons of coal per day were being transported down the canal along withother cargoes of manufactured goods destined for export through the Port of Swansea. Meanwhile cargoes of imported metal ores and locally mined coal were carried up the Swansea Valley to the various metal manufacturing works which lay alongside the route of the canal. Other cargoes included limestone, pit props, pottery, brick, stone and clay. The rapid growth in coal exports carried on the canal can be seen from the following:[3]

1804	54,235 tonnes
1816	159,633 tonnes
1825	208,433 tonnes
1839	386,058 tonnes

Upon completion of the North Dock in 1852, a lock was built to provide a direct link between the Swansea Canal and the upper basin of the new dock. This replaced the former tidal lock between the canal and the river Tawe. In 1872 the Great Western Railway Company acquired the waterway, paying a sum of £107,666 to the Swansea Canal Navigation Company, plus a further £40,000 to the Duke of Beaufort for the Trewyddfa section of the canal near Morriston.[4]

However, there was increasing competition from the Swansea Vale railway, which appeared around 1845, and later the Great Western Railway's own line, built in 1891, which ran parallel to the canal between Pentrefelen, Morriston, and Swansea, on the west bank of the river Tawe, feeding the copper, coal and manufacturing and industries in the lower Swansea valley.

The origins of the Swansea Vale Railway lay in an early nineteenth century tramroad (Scott's Tramroad on the east bank of the river Tawe). The SVR company was formed to build a modern railway route serving the mines and metal industries in the Swansea Valley, and by 1860 a passenger service between St Thomas's station in Swansea and Pontardawe had been established. By 1864 the line had been extended from Gurnos Junction to Brynamman in the northern coalfield. The southern section of the Morriston Loop, between Upper Bank and Morriston, was opened in 1871 and the northern section to Glais Junction in 1875. The Midland Railway leased the SVR in 1874 and purchased it two years later.[5]

Transporting merchandise by railway was cheaper and quicker than by canal, and this eventually led to a substantial reduction in canal borne traffic. The Swansea Canal showed its first working loss in 1895; its final year of being marginally in profit was 1902, and in 1921 the total amount of cargo carried was just 10,600 tonnes. The lower section of the canal was closed and filled in shortly after the First World War and traffic ceased completely when the last cargo of coal was carried from Hill's Colliery, Clydach, in 1931.[6]

(Plate 3) View of derelict Swansea Canal at Landore. C1960.
The G.W.R. Morriston Branch Line can be seen on the
right hand side of the canal. SS 661956.
Courtesy Gareth Mills Swansea Docks Collection.

In the next Chapter we will examine the role played by the
Swansea Canal in the transportation of coal from the mines in
Treboeth, Brynhyfryd and Landore to the smelting works and
the Port of Swansea by the use of inclined planes.

CHAPTER IX
BIBLIOGRAPHY AND ILLUSTRATIONS

(1) The Glamorgan Historian Vol 6, The Hopkin Thomas
     Project, Coal mining in West Glamorgan, G. Thomas. 1969.
(2) The Economic Development of Swansea and of the
     Swansea District to 1921. D.Trevor Williams. University
     College of Swansea Pamphlet 4. 1940
(3) Gareth Mills, Swansea Canal, Swansea and Port Talbot
     Docks Collection, 2017.

(4) Ibid

(5) B.A.Malaws, RCAHMW, 2012.

(6) Gareth Mills, Swansea Canal, Swansea and Port Talbot Docks Collection, 2017

(Plate 1) Coal tubs and barges moored on the canal at Clydach-on-Tawe dockyard. SS 684005. Courtesy John Hutchings.

(Plate 2) Horse-drawn barge on Swansea Canal at Vivian's Copperworks, Hafod. C1860. SS 660951. Courtesy Swansea Museum Collection

(Plate 3) View of derelict Swansea Canal at Landore C1960 The G.W.R. Morriston Branch Line can be seen on the right hand side of the canal. SS 661956 Courtesy Gareth Mills Swansea Docks Collection.

CHAPTER X

COAL MINING IN TREBOETH, BRYNHYFRYD AND LANDORE

The Treboeth district itself was not immune from such developments: coal mining, which had been taking place in the locality in a limited way for many years, was now expanding rapidly to feed the enormous appetites of the nearby smelting works.

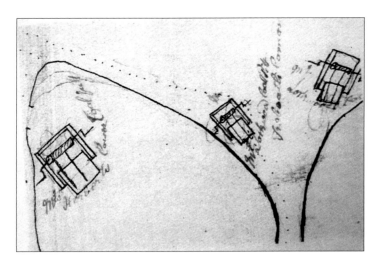

(Plate 1) Early pits and primitive head winding gear at Treboeth.
Courtesy Badmington Collection, Group II, 1454,
National Library of Wales.

Shallow coal pits were in numbers on Treboeth common in the early 18th century: they had simple well-like windlasses set on small timber frames above them. By the early decades of the nineteenth century the local landowners and tenants who had hitherto controlled or worked the industry were being elbowed out by industrialists such as the Morrises and their partners the Lockwoods. As a result, the lower slopes of Treboeth and Landore, with coal mines at Penvilia, Pentre, and the adjacent Cwm Level, together with tramroads, coal-ways and the ever-increasing spoil tips, began to assume the appearance of a coal mining district.

Evidence of Lockwood, Morris & Co's on-going activities seeking reserves of coal in the area can be seen in a 1768 plan for the sinking of a mechanised deeper shaft at Tirdeunaw Colliery, Treboeth. The plan required the installation of a horse powered gin for lowering and raising coal. (Plate 2)

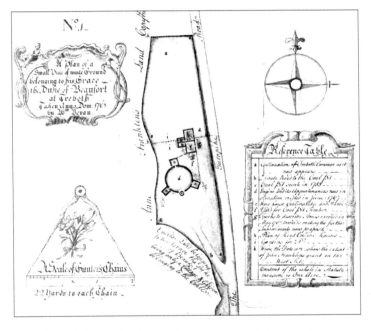

(Plate 2) 1768 Plan for sinking of a deeper shaft at Tirdeunaw Colliery, Treboeth. The plan required the installation of a horse powered gin for lowering and raising coal. SS 665290. Courtesy Badmington Collection Group II 1281. National Library of Wales.

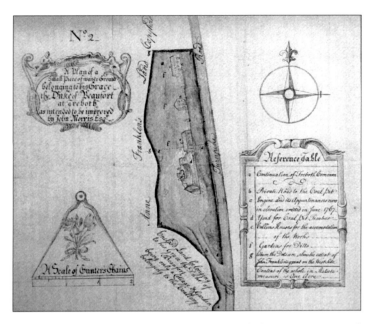

(Plate 3) Drawings of the five colliers' houses which were to constructed on the colliery site next to thr horse-gin in 1769. Courtesy Badmington Collection Group II 1282 & 1283 National Library of Wales.

The Tirdeunaw (Treboeth) Pit Colliery, which opened in late 1768, was sited on the north side of Treboeth common. Freeholders held the rights to the minerals under their own land, but the Duke of Beaufort claimed the minerals under the commons and copyhold lands and this applied to much of the land covering the coalfield. Interestingly, a receipt from the Forest Copperworks for the year 1778–1778 (Plate 3) shows that John Morris purchased coal valued at £498. 47 from the common and copy-hold land tenants of Treboeth, suggesting that the Clyndu Level Colliery's production was insufficient for the works. Indeed, a two-one blend of steam coal and bituminous coal was becoming acceptable by the smelters to meet their production needs.The Duke of Beaufort, being the landowner, would have claimed a wey or levy on this amount.

Coal from Treboth Common and ye Coppyhold Lands Adjoining

1778	W	Load		1779	W	Load	
Oct. 31	38	25		April 24	43	47	
Nov. 28	30	1		May 29	52	3	
Dec. 26	26	33		June 26	49	23	
1779				July 31	59	15	
Jan. 30	38			August 28	43	26	
Feb. 27	35	27		Sep. 25	46	1	
March 27	36	40					
	204	32			294	15	498.47

(Plate 4) Account of coal from Treboth Common and in Coppyhold Lands Adjoining 1778–1779. This was attached to the Fire Engine Coalery account receipt (See Chapter VII Plate 2). Courtesy National Library of Wales.

The sites of the principal Landore collieries can be seen on Plate 3 and comprised Penfilia, Cwm and Cwm Level, Pentre and Calland's.

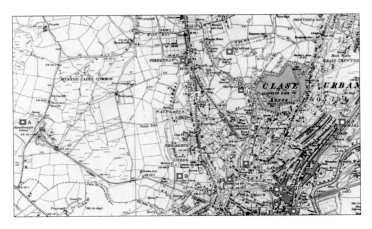

(Plate 5) Map of past Landore District Coal Pits.

'A' Mynydd Newydd, 'B' Tirdeunaw, 'C' Clase, 'D' Penfilia, 'E' Pentre, 'F' Cwm Level, 'G' Callands, 'H' Plasmarl, 'I' Landore, 'J' Cwm Gelli. (Note the map does not show Tirdonkin and Cefngyfelach collieries sited near Llangyfelach). Courtesy O.H.M.S.

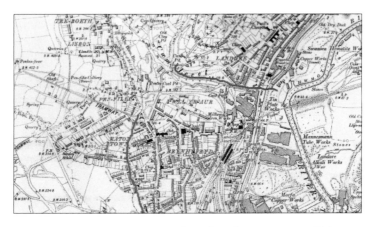

(Plate 6) 1889 O.S. Map of Landore showing routes of John Morris's inclined tramway RED from Cwm Pit along Cwm level Road and joining his Pentre Colliery tramway and incline to Swansea Canal coaling wharf, and Eaton Road tramway BLUE leading to the Pottery and the Port of Swansea. Courtesy O.H.M.S

The area which surrounds Treboeth/Brynhyfryd and Landore was also rich in bituminous coal, and below ground were lucrative veins of coal known as the Five foot, Six Foot, Three Foot and Two Foot seams, which mirrored the developments in mining and copper smelting taking place further up the Tawe valley near Morriston.

CWM LEVEL AND CWM PIT

Cwm collieries were worked as early as 1736, when adits (horizontal shafts) were driven into the hillside, forming levels for draining the workings as well as providing ways to transport the extracted coal. These were often found within vertical shafts. Beneath these levels, whimsies (devices for lifting coal) were used rather then a steam engine. Some adits were almost a mile in length, admitting low wagons running on iron tramways, each wagon holding a chaldron of coal. This measure, originating in the 13th century, and only abolished in 1963, varies widely in in different areas. In London it was the equivalent of 28 cwt, while in the north of England it could be as much as 53 cwt. Whatever standard was used locally, loaded waggons could be delivered to the quay by using one horse. [1]

Cwm Level, opened in 1736 and Cwm Pit, opened in 1803, were close to each other at the bottom end of Trewyddfa Road. Both were in the Duke of Beaufort's mineral estate which covered Treboeth, Trewyddfa and Cadley commons.

(Plate 7) View of Cwm Pit, following closure. Note the large engine house. The remains of Morris's Tenament 'Castle' can be seen on the hill. SS 656961. Courtesy Swansea Museum Collection.

Cwm Pit lay within a couple of hundred yards of the Pentre Pit and is probably to be equated with ,Mr. Morris' Level' which is marked on old estate maps of the late eighteenth century. The site is now occupied by the Roman Catholic Church of St. Peter, Landore, which was opened in 1927.

Cwm Pit was the earliest of the levels opened out in the Landore-Brynhyfryd area and operated with a water wheel winder. In 1803 a steam pump was built at the pit but winding by water power continued until the end of the nineteenth century. Pentre Pit was also connected to Cwm Level. The Pentre colliery stables were near the mouth of the old Cwm Level, enabling the horses to come to the surface through the 'horse way', as it was called. Underground was a sort of staircase known as the horse road, which must have been the connection from the Pentre pit Six Foot seam workings to the Cwm Pit Five Foot seam [Penvilia] workings.[1]

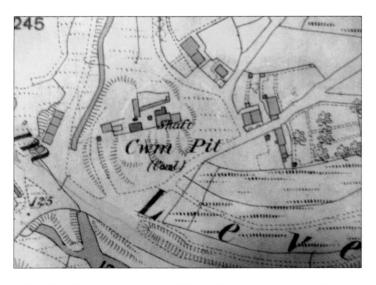

(Plate 8) 1876 O.S. Site Map of Cwm Pit site. Courtesy O.H.M.S.

In 1803, John Morris II took a lease on the Beaufort Six Foot and Three Foot seams for 42 years, his centre of operations being Cwm Pit. He installed a winding and pumping engine from Trevithick, replacing the water wheel winder,which also drained the Six Foot and Three Foot seams in Pentre Colliery.[2]

Arthur Pendarves Vivian visited these four colleries in 1868 and reported:

"Cwm Level lay within a couple of hundred yards of the Pentre Pit and is probably equated with Mr. Morris's level which is marked on old estate maps of the late eighteenth century. The main drift of the colliery will be driven through many upthrows and down throw faults going north, and will work the 6 ft. vein below to the solid, in the same ground in which Cwm Level has already worked the 5 ft. above. For this reason we went there next to see the nature of this ground. Cwm Level is driven in the 5ft. where it crops not very far from the Pentre Pit a little below towards Calland's Pit and to the S.E. it runs in level course about North West. We went in the trams about 1 1/2 miles – the 5ft.looks very well here and cuts nice and large and the measures look quiet and at an easy angle. We crossed over one fault, a 1 fathom upturn west. This ground is all full of old workings and there are no less than 5 levels driven in this neighbourhood in this vein of which one is Clyndu.[Clyndu Level Colliery] They are in fact in this level only scraping out the leavings of the old people."[3]

The Cwm Level Railway ran some 800 yards along the valley at Landore, from the pit to a wharf on the navigable river Tawe via an incline and tunnel. The railway was originally built by Calvert Richard Jones between 1768 and 1770. In all probability John Morris bought the railway and built a short branch south of Cwm Level to his own level at Penfilia. By 1803, Cwm Pit was enlarged and a short branch line built to connect it to the railway which ran to the Landore wharves.[4]

Unlike most lines in south Wales at this time, it was an edge railway, i.e. with flanges on the wheels of the trams. The technology used was that of modern-style railway, but using a three-rail system, in which the centre rail was shared by the up and down lines. However, the operations at Pwll yr Ayr lasted until 1780 when they were abandoned, with the result that the workings flooded. John Morris bought Townsend's pit and tramway in the early nineteenth century and connected it by a branch-line to the head of the Cwm Level.[5]

Between 1845 and 1876 a rectangular dock was built on the Swansea Canal as a loading point for coal boats going south from the Cwm Pit Railway. The waterway was then funnelling the coal output from four railways/tramways in the Landore area to fuel the new large scale smelting industry at Hafod and Morfa.[6]

Interestingly, in 1854 when John Morris leased the mining assets of Cwm Pit to Glasbrook and Richard, they comprised the following:

"AT CWM PIT Boiler and fittings 34 feet long by five feet diameter complete. 36 inch pumping Engine of low pressure complete except the nozels and gearing. 80 fathoms of pumps and rods complete. Great. and capstan shaft complete." [7]

PENTRE COLLIERY

The first Pentre colliery began in 1745 at a site behind St. John's Road, Manselton. It was owned by Thomas Price, the coal owner squire of Penllegaer. From 1746, Morris and Lockwood showed an interest in the Brynhyfryd area. They worked coal under a lease from the Duke of Beaufort, with pits and levels at Landore, Plasmarl, Clyndu and Treboeth, mainly to supply their copper smelting works at Forest.[8]

When Thomas Price died in 1768, Pentre colliery passed to his son, Griffith Price. The colliery was found to be unworkable without a 'fire engine' so he built an atmospheric steam engine to pump out the water flooding the mine workings. His lease from the Duke of Beaufort expired in 1785, but he had wisely taken out a reversionary lease to ensure he remained in possession of the colliery. Price worked the Five Foot seam continuously until the end of 1787, when production averaged 10,457 tonnes a year almost exhausting the seam.[9]

Following his death in the same year, his executors assigned the lease in January 1788 to Lockwood and Morris Co. They found the coal worked out and were forced to sink two of the pits much deeper, at the same time erecting another fire engine, and sinking two new tunnels or drifts to get at the remaining coal. Over the next seven years to November 1795, production rose to an annual average of 16,394 tonnes.[10]

Adjacent to Price's land was the 500-acre estate which had come jointly to Calvert Richard Jones through his marriage. In 1770 he started to sink what was known as Penvilia Pit. It was 40 fathoms deep and continued to be worked by his son, the second Calvert Richard Jones, but the precise location is not known. In 1793, Lockwood and Morris Co. transferred their copper smelting activities from Forest back to Landore and ceased to have any claim to the first Pentre colliery. In March 1797 they took a 21-year lease from Calvert Richard Jones II on the minerals under the Pentre estate. In 1800, however, Morris withdrew from the partnership, and the firm became simply Lockwood and Co., a family name.[11] The pit survived until its closure in 1924.

Penvilia level was west of Llangyfelach Road, just north of Brynhyfryd Square. From 1800, Lockwood continued to work the Pentre Colliery Five Foot [Penvilia] seam through the Penvilia level. To get down to the Six Foot and Three Foot seams, however, the company needed to sink a shaft which would have to be drained through the Duke of Beaufort's pumping engine at Callands pit, Landore. In 1802 Lockwood was granted a 26 year lease of this famous engine. Ironically, Lockwood and Morris Co. had started to build this engine in the 1790's, but it had passed into the possession of the Duke of Beaufort in 1798 when they forfeited the Six Foot and Three Foot seams. This had come about because they failed to work the coal after the workings were flooded by water, which had broken through from an adjoining colliery.[12]

In 1803, John Morris II took on a 42 year lease of the Beaufort Six Foot and Three Foot seams, and started to develop Cwm Pit. He installed winding and pumping engines, and in around 1805 he relaid an earlier inclined tramway, which had originally been built by Calvert Richard Jones in 1770 to serve his Penvilia Pit. Unlike most lines in south Wales at this time, it was an edge railway i.e. with flanges on the wheels of the trams. The technology used on was that of modern-style railway, but using a three-rail system, in which the centre rail was shared by the up and down lines. Trains of climbing and descending wagons were linked by a continuous cable which ran on a series of rollers and guides along the centre of the tracks. At the top of each incline the cable passed through a braking system which controlled the trains' speed. In the middle of each incline, the centre rail divided into a conventional double track layout, so that the trains could pass. This 'modern' style railway design was later used on the Mynydd Newydd and Pentrefelen railroads.

The Cambrian reported the effectiveness of the Pentre inclined plane:

"IMPROVEMENTS IN RAILROADS. It is with pleasure we notice that the improvements introduced by the match of mechanical intellect in the north of England are rapidly extending themselves in this part of the country. Last week an improved railway and self- acting inclined plane, of nearly half a mile in length, were opened in the immediate neighbourhood of Swansea, which appear to merit the inspection of the scientific and curious in these matters. The plane is much faster than anything before seen in this part of the country, being at an inclination of only about two inches in a yard; it is remarkable for having in its length two curves, somewhat in the shape of a letter S, which the engineer thought necessary to adopt to avoid a deep ravine on one side and a hill in the other. The rails are of cast iron, on their edge, are dove-tailed at each end, and wedged into cast-iron pedestals, which are again secured by bars of iron transversely across the road, forming, in fact, at each interval two pedestals in one casting, which serve to connect the two parallel rails, and to keep the road always in gauge – a most desirable object. These pedestals are secured in the usual manner to large solid blocks of stone. The inclined plane connects the Pentre Colliery, the property of the Landore Colliery Company, with the Swansea canal, and has been formed at considerable expense, the embankment being in some parts above twenty feet high. It is perfectly astonishing to see with what rapidity and precision in it does its work, ten tons of coal being passed a time over the space of nearly half a mile in two minutes, being a rate of 15 miles per hour. Thus this simple arrangement would enable the proprietors, if their demand required it, allowing an interval of three minutes each time for casting off and reconnecting the empty and full waggons, to send down 120 tonnes of coal in an hour. In this rich mineral district it would seem due advantage has not yet been taken of desending levels from many of our most valuable mines," [13]

This gave Morris an outlet to the Swansea Canal at Landore, allowing him to ship his coal either north to the copperworks or south to Swansea Harbour for shipping. It also showed that Lockwood was working the Beaufort Five Foot (Penvilia) seams and Morris was workg the Six Foot and Three Foot seams with his operations centred on Cwm Pit. (See page 34 During that same year Lockwood started to sink the second Pentre pit. It was sunk 72 fathoms to the Six Foot and Three Foot seams, to win a large area which hitherto had remained untouched. A drift was driven into the Three Foot seam still lower to serve as a water course and drain. Production started in 1807 under the first manager, John Jeremiah.[14]

E.D. Clarke, during his tour through the South of England and Wales and Part of Ireland in 1793, visited the Pentre colliery and reported:

"Pentre Colliery, belonging to J.Morris: the whole hill (Trewydda) is full of coal and is obtained by what miners term open adits i.e. Horizontal shafts driven into the hill, which form levels for draining the work as well as way for the delivery of coal. These are within some vertical shafts beneath these levels, and whimser (i.e. a capstan or windlass) for raising coal by the weight of water which descending in one bucket draws up another filled with coal have given way to a more philosophical and expedious machine the improved steam engine of Boulton & Watt. One of these adits which we traced about a mile in length admits low wagons, holding a chauldron each, which running on an iron railway, one horse with ease delivers at the quay [at Landore]."[15]

Moreover, the Rev J Evans, writing during his tour of South Wales in 1804, commented:

"At the Pentre Pit, Landore in 1788 there were 240 tonnes of cast iron tram plates underground and before the close of the C18 a Boulton and Watt steam-engine had been installed at a cost of £5000, which was described in the following terms in 1802; this machine throws up from a vast depth 100 gallons of water each stroke, which is repeated twelve times a minute, making 78,000 galls of water per hour."[16]

Eric Svedenstierna, during his visit to Landore in 1802-3 where he saw the machine, commented:

"The engine at Clandover [Landore] deserves special mention. It was built according to Boulton & Watt's latest patent, with the strength of 70 to 80 horses and lifted the water out of a coal mine from a depth of 48 fathoms. The pumps had a diameter of 20 inches and the stroke was between 8 and 9 feet. The normal speed was 12 to 13 strokes per minute; it could, however, in an emergency be taken up to 60. It was calculated that it moved overall 1,100 gallons or almost 1,500 Swedish quarts in a minute, which amounted to between 80,000 and 90,000 quarts per hour."[17]

166

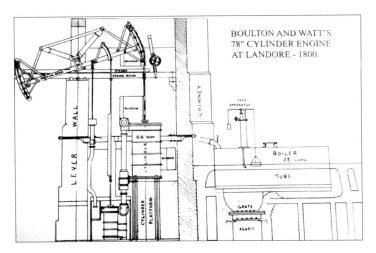

(Plate 9) Drawing of Boulton and Watts 78 inch Cylinder Engine at Landore – 1800. Courtesy Hadyn Holloway, Boulton & Watt Collection, Birmingham Reference Library.

Indeed, by the end of the century the pit had become a tourist attraction.

However, on 9 January 1816, a local newpaper reported that a serious accident had occured at the mine killing two men and "dreadfully burned five others two of which are not expected to survive."

When Arthur Pendarves Vivian visited the Pentre pit in 1868, he reported:

"THE PENTRE PIT is sunk down 72 fathoms on to the 6 foot to win a large bit of ground in this vein which has not been touched beside what can be got out of the old workings. A drift has been driven in the 3ft. vein still lower down in the measures, which is to serve as the watercourse and drain of this colliery and at our boundary this drift has only been lately opened out again, but it is an old drift made by the old people but filled up like a gob with rubbish, not open probably for a century and the rubbish now forms a solid concrete mass like (?), though not so hard as if entrenched (?). This colliery will probably have to be ventilated by driving Mynydd Newydd down to the 6 ft. (now only sunk to the 5 ft.), a depth of 76 fathoms between these two veins. The winding engine on the top of the pit is a 32 inch cylinder, 7 ft. stroke, with a very neat crank overhead motion instead of the usual parallel motion carried out by rods. The main drift of the colliery will be driven through many up-throw and downthrow faults."[18]

Although John Morris and Thomas Lockwood operated separately, friendly relations existed. They shared pumping arrangements with Morris's Cwm engine, draining both workings and the Landore engine, which was leased to Lockwood discharging the accumulated water. They also collaborated over coal transportation. In 1790, Lockwood built a tramway from Pentre to the top of Cwm Burlais to join the Cwm railway which led to Swansea Harbour. In about 1806, Morris built a spur line from Brynhyfryd to serve Cwm Pit.[19]

Much of the course of the railway (tramway) has now been obliterated, but one interesting feature still survives; the Cwm-bridge in the Hafod, where Neath Road passes over Cwm Road. The bridge originally consisted of three arches. The large central arch was for the public road; the arch on the west, which has been covered over, was for the Burlais Brook; while that on the east was intended for Glasbrook's railway (tramway) and before that Morris's Tramway (See Plate 7).

(Plate 10) Cwm Bridge, Hafod Swansea. The eastern arch to the right was used by both Morris's and Glasbrook's tramways on their route to the Pottery and Swansea Harbour.
SS 657942 (c) J.P.Thomas.

Today's Eaton Road preserves the alignment of Lockwood's tramway. Where the Cwm and Pentre branches came together at the top of the road, and storage sidings and a marshalling yard laid out where down wagons could wait for haulage to the harbour and where up wagons could be sorted back to their originating collieries. It is interesting to note that an old name for the sidings was 'Heol-y-Rails.' Morris retained the Eaton tramroad for his Cwm pit traffic until his way-leave in the Cwm expired in 1845 and the tramroad was lifted.

(Plate 11) View of Eaton Road. Manselton, which housed a tramway coal marshalling yard during, where wagons were assembled prior to their journey via Cwm Burlais to the Swansea Harbour. 19 September 2017. SS 654957 (c) J.P.Thomas.

However, in 1825, a tragic accident which occurred at the junction of the two branch tramways shed some light on operating practices. The grammar has not been changed in the following passage: "on Friday se'nnight, an inquest was held by Chas. Collins Esq. body of John Terry, a boy about eight years of age, who came to his death under the following distressing circumstances: – It appeared from the evidence of Morgan Rees, waggoner that on 14th instant.he was driving eight tram–waggons, laden with coals from the Cwm Pit Colliery, when the deceased, with several other children, got on the 5th waggon from the horses – that at the turning of the road near the Pentre, he stopped his waggons, for the purpose of allowing son pass, and on again starting them, the deceased fell off, when the three hind–most waggons, passed over him, by which he had a thigh, leg and arm broken, one of his hands dreadfully shattered, and otherwise so much injured that he died on the following Thursday in great agony. The Jury returned a verdict of Accidental Death, with a deodand on the waggons of 5s. The witness was cautioned not to permit children to ride on his waggons in future."[20]

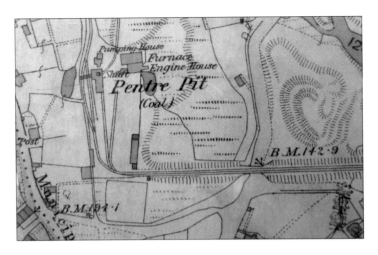

(Plate 12) 1879 coloured O.S. Site Plan of Pentre Pit, Landore, showing three line railroad incline leading to Swansea Canal wharf and coal staithe. SS 654959 Courtesy O.H.M.S.

(Plate 13) 1830 Picture of Pentre Pit Railroad Embankment and Bridge, Landore, at same location as Plate showing three-rail tramway incline leading to Swansea Canal wharf and coal staithe. Cwm Level can be seen in the background. SS 654959 Courtesy University of Wales Swansea Library & Information Services Archives.

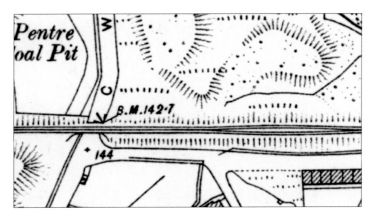

(Plate 14) 1879 O.S. Map of 3-rail Pentre Pit Railroad showing bridge crossing at Cwm Level Road and passing loop.
SS 654959 Courtesy O.H.M.S.

(Plate 15) The route of the Pentre Pit 3-rail Railroad, having crossed Cwm Level Road, followed an embankment running parallel with Cwm Lan Terrace (seen here) before crossing the valley floor and join-ing up with Calvert Jones' former inclined tramroad to Landore quay.
SS 654959. May 2018. (c) J.P.Thomas.

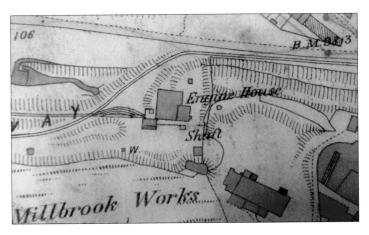

(Plate 16) 1ˢᵗ Edition 1879 coloured O.S. Map of Cwm Valley showing the route of Pentre Colliery Tramway crossing the valley floor joining the truncated section of Calvert Jones's original Cwm Level Tramway to Landore river wharf. Courtesy O.H.M.S.

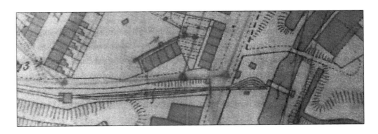

(Plate 17) 1879 coloured O.S. Map showing Pentre Pit Railroad Incline Terminus at Swansea Canal showing wharf, coal staithe and sidings. SS 662961. Courtesy O.H.M.S.

(Plate 18) Pentre Pit Landore showing pit head and beam winding engine C1800. SS654959. Courtesy F.Cowley.

There were also frequent mining accidents in the district. A letter from Morriston, dated 2 September, 1786 describes one such incident:

"A dreadful Explosion, as loud or louder than the heaviest Discharge of Artillery, took Place in Messrs. Lockwood, Morris and Co's. Colliery, [probably the 'Pentre'] occasioned by a Quantity of inflammable Air, and which one William Young, at the Head of a Gang of Colliers, had set Fire to with a Candle, not conscious of the Quantity that was collected; by which Accident the Man, with four others were killed on the Spot, one Man had his Thigh and another his Leg broke, and two or three were much burnt and bruised. The colliery was at Landore"[(21)]

However, mining operations in Landore caused environmental damage on a large scale. Like the copper smelters, who dumped their waste slag in any available space, the mine owners did the same as the following pictures show:

174

(Plate 19) 1955 View of the Nant Gelli at Pwll Cwm looking in the direction of the disused Cwm Level Pit. The rows of terraced houses on the left of the picture are situated in Cwm Lan Terrace. Note the heaps of colliery waste looming above the stream. SS 657959. Courtesy Treboeth Historical & Pictorial Record.Treboeth Historical Society.

Little wonder, then, why Cwm Level Road was known locally as the 'Black Road'.

(Plate 20) View of Cwm Lan Terrace May 2018. The coal waste tips, the polluted stream, and the remains of Cwm Level pit head and stack have all disappeared. The area has been landscaped providing sports facilities and a children's park. SS 657959. (c) J.P. Thomas.

(Plate 21) 1930s View of Penfilia Terrace, Brynhyfryd where there once existed a busy 3- rail tramroad junction, with lines branching out to the district's collieries. It was probably the source of the colliery waste shown dumped in the street. Apparently the small building was a convenience for the use of colliery surface workers. SS 654958. Courtesy Treboeth Historical & Pictorial Record.Treboeth Historical Society.

(Plate 22) View of Penfilia Terrace May 2018. Apart from the newly built garden wall and the absence of coal waste and the workers' convenience, little has changed. SS 654958 (c) J.P. Thomas.

In the next chapter we will look at the contribution made by Callands, Clase, Cwmgelli and Treboeth Level collieries. in ensuring the smelters had sufficient supplies of bituminous coal.

CHAPTER X
BIBLIOGRAPHY AND ILLUSTRATIONS

(1) Treboeth Historical & Pictorial Record. Treboeth Historical Society, 2012. p.105

(2) Ibid. p.106

(3) Welsh Journals on Line, Gower, Vol 24 1973,'The Vivian Collieries in 1868 F. G. Cowley, p.80

(4) Copperopolis. Landscapes of the Early Industrial Period in Swansea. S. Hughes. RCAHMW, 2000,p.303

(5) Swansea History Project, 4 Site Education, Tramroads and Industrial Railways, Paul Reynolds and Gerald Gabb, 2012, p.27 Swansea Refereence Library

(6) S. Hughes, Copperopolis p.308.

(7) Second sheet of Deed Parchment with Schedule of Mining Assets contained in John Morris's 1854 Lease to Glasbrook and Richard Courtesy West Glamorgan Archives Ref: D/D SB 15/56 Details of this lease appear in Chapter XIV

(8) Treboeth Historical & Pictorial Record. Treboeth Historical Society, 2012. P.125

(9) Ibid

(10) Ibid p.128

(11) Ibid

(12) Ibid p.130

(13) Cambrian 5 June 1830

(14) Treboeth Historical & Pictorial Record.Treboeth Historical Society, 2012. p. 129

(15) E.D. Clarke During his tour through the South of England and Wales and Part of Ireland. 1793. P.207. Minerva Press.

(16) Rev J. Evans 'Descriptive Excursions through South Wales and Monmouthshire the Year 1804 and the Four Preceding Summers.'1804, p.165

(17) Eric Svedenstierna, Svedenstierna's Tour of Great Britain 1802–3, The Travel Diary of an Industrial Spy. David & Charles, 1973, pp. 38–49.

(18) Welsh Journals on Line, Vol.24 1973. Vivian Collieries in 1868 F.G.Cowley. p82–84. 1973. (Coal Account Book Vivian Collection of Manuscripts GRO MS No. D/D/GC/6A) (19) Treboeth Historical & Pictorial Record. Treboeth Historical Society, 2012. p. 129 (2) (20)Cambrian 30 July 1825 – The grammar has not been altered.

(21) A letter from Morriston, dated 2 September, 1786, describes one such incident.

(Plate 1) Shallow coal pits were in numbers on Treboeth common in the early 18th century: they had simple well-like windlasses set on small timber frames above them. Courtesy Badmington Collection Group II 1454 National Library of Wales. See S.R. Hughes, Collieries in Wales. Engineering and Architecture, RCAHW, 1994.

(Plate 2) 1768 Plan for sinking of a deeper shaft at Tirdeunaw Colliery, Treboeth. The plan required the installation of a horse powered gin for lowering and raising coal. SS 665290. Courtesy National Library of Wales. Badmington Collection II 1281. See S.R. Hughes, Collieries in Wales. Engineering and Architecture, RCAHW, 1994.

(Plate 3) Drawings of the five colliers' houses which were to constructed on the colliery site next to the horse-gin in 1769. Courtesy Badmington Collection Group II 1282 & 1283 National Library of Wales. See S.R. Hughes, Collieries in Wales. Engineering and Architecture, RCAHW, 1994.

(Plate 4) Account of Coal from Treboeth Common and in Coppyhold Lands Adjoining 1778–1779.

(Plate 5) Map of past Landore District Coal Pits.

(Plate 6) 1889 O.S. Map of Landore showing routes of John Morris's tramway RED from Cwm Pit along Cwm level Road and joining his Pentre Colliery tramway with an incline to the Swansea Canal coaling wharf, and theEaton Road tramway BLUE leading to the Pottery and the Port of Swansea. Courtesy O.H.M.S.

(Plate 7) View of Cwm Level Pit, following closure. Note the large engine house. SS 656961. Courtesy Treboeth, Historical and Pictorial Record, Treboeth Historical Society, 2012. p. 129.

(Plate 8) 1876 O.S. Site Map of Cwm Coal Pit site.

(Plate 9) Drawing of Boulton and Watts 78 inch Cylinder Engine at Landore – 1800. Courtesy Hadyn Holloway, Boulton & Watt Collection, Birmingham Reference Library.

(Plate 10) Cwm Bridge, Hafod Swansea. The eastern arch to the right was used by both Morris's and Glasbrook's tramways on their route to the Pottery and Swansea Harbour. SS 657942 (c) J.P.Thomas.

(Plate 11) View of Eaton Road. Manselton, which housed a tramway coal marshalling yard, where waggons were assembled prior to their journey via Cwm Burlais to the Swansea Harbour. 19 September 2017. SS 654957 (c) J.P.Thomas.

(Plate 12) 1879 O.S. Site Plan of Pentre Pit, Landore, showing three line railroad incline leading to Swansea Canal wharf and coal staithe. SS 654959. Courtesy O.H.M.S.

(Plate 13) 1830 Picture of Pentre Pit Railroad Embankment and Bridge, Landore, at same location as Plate showing three-rail tramway incline leading to Swansea Canal wharf and coal staithe. Cwm Level Pit can be seen in the background. SS 654959. Courtesy University of Wales Swansea Library & Information Services Archives.

(Plate 14) 1879 O.S. Map of 3-rail Pentre Pit Railroad showing Bridge Crossing and Passing Loop. SS 654959 Courtesy O.H.M.S.

(Plate 15) Remains of former 3-rail Pentre Pit Railroad embankment running parallel with Cwm Lan Terrace, Landore, leading to Swansea Canal wharf, coal staithe and sidings. SS 654959 (c) J. P. Thomas. 15 March 2018.

(Plate 16) 1st Edition 1879 coloured O.S. Map of Cwm Valley showing the route of Pentre Colliery Tramway crossing

the valley floor joining the truncated section of Calvert
Jones's original Cwm Level Tramway to Landore river
wharf.

(Plate 17) 1879 O.S. Map showing Pentre Pit Railroad Incline
Terminus at Swansea Canal showing wharf, coal staithe
and sidings. SS 662961. Courtesy O.H.M.S.

(Plate 18) Pentre Pit Landore showing Pit Head and Beam
Winding Engine C1800. SS 654959. Courtesy F. Cowley.

(Plate 19) 1955 View of the Nant Gelli at Pwll Cwm looking in the direction of the disused Cwm Level Pit. The
rows of terraced houses on the left of the picture are situated in Cwm Lan Terrace.Note the heaps of colliery waste
looming above the stream. SS 657959. Courtesy Treboeth
Historical & Pictorial Record.Treboeth Historical Society,
2012. p.97.

(Plate 20) View of Cwm Lan Terrace May 2018. The coal
waste tips, the polluted stream, and the remains of Cwm
Level pit head and stack have all disappeared. The area has
been landscaped providing sports facilities and a children's
park. SS 657959. (c) J.P. Thomas.

(Plate 21) 1930,s View of Penfilia Terrace, Brynhyfryd where
there once existed a busy tramroad junction with lines
branching out to the district's collieries, probably the
source of the colliery waste shown dumped in the street.
Apparently the small building was a convenience for
the use of colliery surface workers. SS 654958 Courtesy
Treboeth Historical & Pictorial Record.Treboeth
Historical Society, 2012. P.132

(Plate 22) View of Penfilia Terrace May 2018. Apart from the
newly built garden wall and the absence of coal waste and
the workers' convenience, little has changed. SS 654958
(c) J.P. Thomas.

CHAPTER XI

CALLANDS, CLASE, CWMGELLI AND TREBOETH LEVEL COLLIERIES

Callands Pit was crucial to the workings of several collieries. Situated almost 450 yards east of Pentre, it was originally sunk as a coal shaft in 1762, but from 1805 it was used by John Morris II, in conjunction with the Duke of Beaufort's Landore engine, as a pumping shaft to drain all the workings on the western side of the Tawe valley. A Newcomen engine was installed in the 'fire-engine pit' in 1776 NTP pump through a 12 inch bore, but the pit was drowned in 1794. In 1800 a new 25 horsepower Boulton and Watt engine was installed, pumping through an 18 ½ inch bore. The 65 inch cylinder had an 8–9 foot stroke, moving 1,100 gallons of water per minute with 12–13 strokes.[1] This was complimented by a Trevithick high pressure steam winding engine with an 8 inch diameter cylinder, working at 40–50 p.s.i.

(Plate 1) 1930 Photograph showing remains of Callands's Pit, including the famed engine house. SS 662959. Courtesy Aerofilms.

In the early 1850s the Pentre mineral estate was assigned to the Swansea Coal Company (See Chapter XIV), which thus acquired Callands Pit. In 1858 the company reconstructed the engine house and installed a magnificient new Cornish beam engine. There were two shafts, one for pumping and one for a cage used for raising coal, when the Six Foot and Three Foot seams were worked.

At the time of John Morris's lease of mining assets to Glasbrook and Richard in 1854, those at Callands Pumping Pit were recorded as:

"AT LANDORE PUMPING PIT Two Boilers and fittings 30 feet long by 6 feet Diameter complete. An old cylinder fit for a casing for a smaller engine. Engine House. Great. A pump pit and rods and two old capstans."[2]

The Swansea Coal Company (See Chapter XIV) was dissolved in 1863 and most of its assets, including Callands Pit, were transferred to Vivian and Sons, owners of the Hafod Morfa Copperworks. The company continued to operate the former collieries of the Swansea Coal Co., but as coal supplies became exhausted they were closed down or sold. In 1812, Vivian and Sons sub-leased Pentre Pit and Calland's Pit to Pentre Collieries and Brickworks Ltd. with the requirement that they continued to pump the workings as before.

In 1924 Vivians merged with Williams Foster to form British Copper Manufacturers. In the same year Pentre Pit ceased operations and the responsibility for pumping at Calland's Pit reverted to Vivian and Sons. The company subsequently sold their one surviving colliery, Mynydd Newydd, together with Calland's Pit in 1926.

The new company was unable to meet the costs of pumping at Callands on its own and sought the assistance of other colliery owners, whose mine workings were drained by Callands. The Mynydd Newydd Colliery Company took over from Vivian and Sons in July 1926 and the owners kept on pumping for a time, but eventually ceased. As a result, water levels started rise in the entire district. The pit finally closed in 1932.

CLASE PIT

Clase Colliery was located some 50 metres west of the present day Clase Social Club. The shaft was 246 feet deep.

(Plate 2) Clase Pit Shaft Head Gear following closure in 1823.
SS655971. Courtesy Treboeth Historical Society.

The pit was known to locals as Pwll Jones (Jones' Pit) and may have derived its name from David Jones, who once owned a Clase colliery (1852–1857), which was probably on the Morris family's Clasemont estate.

Clase Pit worked the Five Foot [Penvilia] seam and employed 16 men before it was abandoned in October 1923, leaving the winding gear in situate and the shaft uncapped.[3]

CWM GELLI PIT

Cwm Gelli Level was the last mine to be worked in the Nant Cwm Gelli valley. Thomas Richard and Elias Morgan, a well known builder and contractor, formed a company in around 1900 to open a coal level in Cwm Gelli to work the Five-Foot seam. Coal was struck in a trial extraction in April the same year, and the seam was reached on 6 June 1901.[4]

The entrance to the mine was on the eastern bank of Nant Cwm Gelli. A slight rising gradient inwards from the entrance allowed underground mine water to drain into the stream which passes across the mouth of the level.This was common practice in Welsh coal levels. Interestingly the drift mine was known locally as 'Ladysmith' after the famous relief of Ladysmith in February 1900 during the Boer War. It was after this event that coal was struck in the trial heading, hence the name 'Ladysmith' was given to the colliery.[5]

(Plate 3) Abandoned Entrance to Cwm Gelli Drift Mine. December 2008. SS 656971.Courtesy Treboeth Historical Society.

The mine heading worked directly northwards beneath Mynydd Garlwyd Road until the old workings of Clase Pit were reached, where the depth of the seam from the surface was 82 yards. It also worked an area of coal eastwards towards to old working of Trewyddfa Pit. However, on 4 June, 1904, The 'Cambrian' newspaper reported an inquest into the death of John Robert John, aged 19 years, who was killed at the colliery. The inquest was held at Brynhyfryd and was attended by Mr. Robson, mines inspector.

The colliery appears to have worked successfully until 28 September 1906, when the London Gazette announced the winding up of the Company:

"The Companies Consolidation Act, 1908.
The CWMGELLY COLLIERY COMPANY Limited.
AT an Extraordinary General Meeting of the Members of the above named Company, duly convened, and held at Cwmgelly Colliery Office, Landore, R.S.O., Glamorgan, on the 3rd day of May, 1912, the following Extraordinary Resolution was duly That the Company cannot, by reason of its liabilities, continue its business, and it is advisable to wind up the same; and accordingly that the Company be wound up voluntarily, and that Thomas Griffith Thomas, of Gwynfe-Road, Treboeth, Landore, be thereby appointed Liquidator for the purposes of such winding-up. Dated this 13th day of May, 1912.
M. E. MORGAN, Chairman."

Apparently the drift mine continued operations until the end World War 1.

During its operation a tramway was laid from the drift mine to a coal yard near Cwm Level Square, from where coal was hauled away in horse drawn wagons to various works and to coal merchants for sale to householders at 9 shillings per hundredweight.[6]

TREBOETH LEVEL

Treboeth Level was situated on the western bank of Nant-Cwm-Gelli and worked by John Morris before 1775.[7] The souther-ly course of the Treboeth level tramway to Cwm Pit is clear-ly visible on the eastern scarp of lower Cwm Gelli. This ledge was used to carry the Cwm Gelli tramway to a coal distribu-tion yard on the site of the disused Cwm Pit.

The Cwm Pit, Lower Nant Cwm Gelli, and Treboeth coal level tramway was constructed between 1826 and 1838 and joined the tramway branches to Cwm Pit and Treboeth Level at the north eastern end of Milbrook Street, which is also built on its line.

The long sloping sweep of Dinas Street, north of Landore, follows the 'main line' of the Cwm Pit, Lower Nant Cwm Gelli and Treboeth Coal Levels Tramway which supplied coal di-rectly to the Rose, Birmingham, and Forest Copperworks. In around 1844, the Treboeth levels ceased supplying coal to the Forest Copperworks, and by 1855 the tramway was left disused and derelict. The tramway was relaid in the period 1900–1914 as an outlet for the newly opened Cwmgelli Level.[8]

John Morris then formed the Penvilia Vein Company to ex-ploit the collieries at Penvilia, Treboeth and Clyndu. It was this company that then built the Cwm Level, Treboeth Level and Lower Nant Cwm Gelli tramroads to transport coal northwards to supply the Rose, Birmingham and Forest Copperworks di-rectly by tramroad. Previously the coal had been supplied only to Lockwood, Morris and Co.'s Landore Copperworks by a line down the Nan Rhyd-y-Filias Valley.[9] By 1807 a second tram-road (the Penvilia or Pentre II Coal pits and Cwm Pit II tram-road) had been built from the same coal producing area south-wards to an outlet at Swansea which could be reached by 600 tonne sailing vessels.

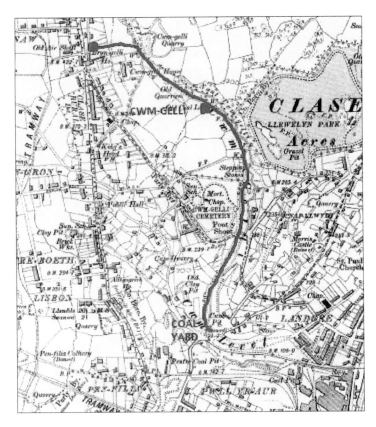

(Plate 4) 1879 O.S. Map showing Tramway and sites of Tirdeunaw (Treboeth) Pit (SS652970) Cwm Gelli Level (SS656960)and Cwm Square Coal Yard. SS656960.

There were also frequent mining accidents in the district. A letter from Morriston, dated 2 September, 1786 describes one such incident:

"A dreadful Explosion, as loud or louder than the heaviest Discharge of Artillery, took Place in Messrs. Lockwood, Morris and Co's. Colliery, [location not known] occasioned by a Quantity of inflammable Air, and which one William Young, at the Head of a Gang of Colliers, had set Fire to with a Candle, not conscious of the Quantity that was collected; by which Accident the Man, with four others were killed on the Spot, one Man had his Thigh and another his Leg broke, and two or three were much burnt and bruised. The colliery was at Landore."[10]

By the mid-1800's all the best supplies of bituminous coal in the lower Swansea Valley were nearing exhaustion, and new reserves were being sought to the west of Swansea. In the next chapter we will look at how John Glasbrook and his brother-in-law, Phillip Richard, exploited the coal reserves in Cwm Burlais.

CHAPTER XI
BIBLIOGRAPHY AND ILLUSTRATIONS

Second sheet of Deed Parchment with Schedule of Mining Assets contained in John Morris's 1854 Lease to Glasbrook and Richard Courtesy West Glamorgan Archives Ref: D/D SB 15/56 Details of this lease appear in Chapter XIV

(1) Svedenstierna 1802 p.46
(2) Treboeth Historical & Pictorial Record.Treboeth Historical Society, 2012. p.103
(3) Ibid p.107
(4) Ibid p.108
(5) Ibid
(6) Copperopolis. Landscapes of the Early Industrial Period in Swansea. S. Hughes. RCAHMW, 2000,p.314
(7) Swansea History Project, 4 Site Education, Tramroads and Industrial Railways, Paul Reynolds and Gerald Gabb, 2012, p.38 Swansea Refereence Library. p.277
(8) Copperopolis. Landscapes of the Early Industrial Period in Swansea. S. Hughes. RCAHMW, 2000,p.312
(9) Northampton Mercury 9 September 1786. Quoted in Gracie's Guide 1997)

(Plate 1) 1930 Photograph showing remains of Callands's Pit, including the famed engine house. Courtesy Aerofilms

(Plate 2) Clase Pit Shaft Head Gear following closure in 1823. Courtesy Treboeth Historical Society.

(Plate 3) Abandoned Entrance to Cwmgelli Drift Mine. December 2008. SS 656971 Courtesy Treboeth Historical Society

(Plate 4) 1879 O.S. Map showing Tramway route and sites of Tirdeunaw Pit SS 652970, Cwmgelli Level, SS 656960 and Cwm Square Coal Yard SS 656960

CHAPTER XII

CWM BURLAIS COLLIERIES

By the 1840s all the best reserves of bituminous coal in the Lower Swansea Valley were nearing exhaustion, and new reserves were being sought to the west of Swansea. It was during this period of shortages of suitable smelting coal that in 1840, a wealthy Loughor mine owner, Nathaniel Cameron, planned to use the Cwm Burlais route for his ambitious Loughor to Swansea Railway which would have required an inclined railway with a rise of 379 feet from the Strand (via two tunnels) to Cockett, and a drop of 269 feet down to Ystrad Isaf in the Llan valley. The intended railway was planned to bring rich bituminous coal from the north Gower coal field to the lower Swansea Valley copper smelting works and to a private wharf in Swansea Harbour for export.

Although Cameron obtained a Parlimentary Act in 1840 for its construction, as shown on the accompanying map, it never materialised, due primarily to the cost of purchasing land and raisng sufficient capital for the construction works. He was eventually declared bankrupt for failing to pay rent on the private wharf.

In 1848, John Glasbrook and his brother-in-law, Phillip Richard, were in the process of developing their new Gorse colliery near Cockett, and made an application to Swansea Corporation for permission to lay a railway in the Cwm between the Pottery and Pentre Bridge. This was to be on the same alignment as Morris's tramroad of 1790, which had been lifted in 1839.[1]

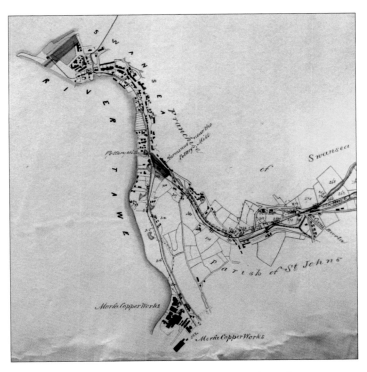

(Plate 1) 1840 Map of Nathaniel Cameron's planned Swansea to Loughor Railway which followed the line of the Burlais Brook with lines extending from the Pottery to Vivian's Hafod and Morfa Copperworks and Swansea Harbour.
Courtesy Glamorgan Archives J.P.Thomas October 2017.

Permission for this railway would have been a formality, since the line had been built from the Pottery (where coal could then be loaded into vessels on the river Tawe) to Cwmbwrla by 1849. The reinstated line enabled Glasbrook and Richard to transport coal directly to vessels on the river Tawe for shipping.[2]

Their line began at the Swansea Pottery wharfs and, in its initial years, ran to Cwmbwrla only. In the mid–1850s it was extended to the Gorse and Weig Fawr collieries by means of an inclined plane at Cave Street, which operated on the self acting principle, with the coal wagons being raised and lowered by chains.The branch to the Worcester and Weig Fach collieries was built during the 1860s, striking off from the Gorse line just above the incline.[3]

In 1863 an elderly man was killed on this incline: he had been at work repairing the track and, as the wagons started to be lowered, he failed to see the movement of the chains or to hear the warning shouts of his companions.[4]

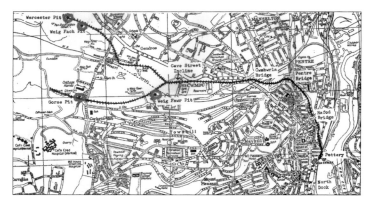

(Plate 2) O.S. Map showing routes of Glasbrook and Richard's Cwm Burlais Tramways to Weig Fawr, Gorse, Weig Fach and Worcester Pits. C.1848–1875. SS 639946 Courtesy Swansea Reference Library. Swansea History Project 4. Note the Author has added the RED colliery markers.

The railway continued to operate throughout the 1850s and 1860s, and occasionally appeared in the local press in connection with accidents. The youth of the district appear to have played on the railway as a regular pursuit, sometimes with fatal consequences:

"A boy was killed in June 1860 in this way, and another in the following September. At the inquest on the latter it was stated that the deceased, like many other boys, was in the habit of getting in the waggons as they come down the Cwmbwrla incline and about 4 o'clock that afternoon he endeavoured to jump upon one of the waggons, and in so doing fell under the wheels and his head was crushed to pieces."[5]

However, it may have been that the boy was killed in the course of duty and not as a result of larking about, for it also stated that he was in the service of Mr. Richard Glasbrook. Another interesting point to emerge from this accident report is that the horses and wagon involved belonged to a Mr. Trevor Williams, which may indicate that Richard and Glasbrook subcontracted their coal haulage to small operators, or was it a case of a member of the public exercising his right to use the railway, as provided for in the terms of the Corporation grant?[6]

Yet another accident occurred in 1871 when a William Marchant was knocked down and run over. Marchant was a stranger to Swansea. He had just arrived from Portsmouth and had been offered a job at the Cwmbwrla tinplate works. He came out of the works all unsuspecting and stepped onto the incline in front of a train [of coal wagons]. He died the next day of his injuries.[7]

From the Cave Street incline, the railway cut across the open fields that were to become the site of a brickworks, following an alignment to the south of what was to become Ael-y-Bryn. From there, the line headed towards Fforestfach Cross, before cutting across Martell Street and Station Road and heading in an arc towards the Worcester and Weig collieries many years before the pits were connected to the GWR line at Cockett.

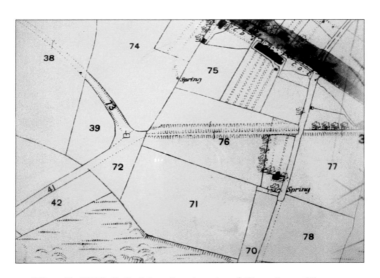

(Plate 3) 1879 O.S. Map showing site of Cave Street Tramway Incline (76) and its 'Y' junction with the tramways (73 & 41) leading to the Worcester and Gorse Collieries. SS 641948. Courtesy O.H.M.S.

The tramway extension to the Weig Fawr and Gorse collieries came in the mid-1850 shortly after the line's completion, while the opening year of the branch to the Weig Fach and Worcester pits is not known. However we know that Thomas Glasbrook (the brother of John) was granted a lease of the Worcester pit by the Duke of Beaufort in 1863. It was not until 1870 that coal was struck at Weig Fach.[8]

WORCESTER COLLIERY, FFORESTFACH

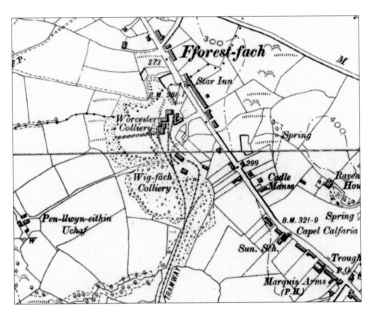

(Plate 4) 1879 O.S. Map Showing Sites of Worcester and New Weig Fach Collieries, Fforestfach, Swansea. The Tramway shown connected the collieries to the GWR at Cockett Station. SS 628956 Courtesy O.H.M.S.

The first sod was cut by Septimus Readhead of the Worcester Coal Company in March 1845. The colliery was worked in conjunction with the Weig Fach Colliery and Pwll Saint or Saint's Pit. The shaft was 100 feet deep and measured 13 feet by 7 feet (rectangular). Ventilation was by means of a 23 feet diameter Waddle fan. It was sold to Thomas Glasbrook in December 1849 who later passed it on to his son Thomas Glasbrook (jnr.) who was granted a lease by the Duke of Beaufort in 1863. The shaft was deepened and in 1864 struck a "vein of highly bituminous coal" (Penvilian). In 1969 the owner is listed as Mr. T. Glasbrook, although in 1877 the colliery was in the hands of Landore Siemens Steel Company and at this time the manager was Mr. T. Glasbrook. The first time the Worcester colliery was yielding coal was in 1866 when an accident was recorded at the pit, while it was not until 1870 that coal was struck at Weig Fach.[9]

There was an explosion at the Weig Fach colliery in early September 1873 which claimed the lives of 4 men. John Howells, 24 years, Joseph Humel, 23 years, William Lake, 42 years and William Thomas, 44 years.

The inquest jury on the explosion recommended the immediate removal of the fireman who had been in charge. He had found gas in the workings 2 hours previous to the blast but still allowed the colliers to work there. The company obviously didn't act on this advice as the same fireman was in charge and lost his life in the second explosion at the Weig Fach colliery several years later.[10]

The colliery was prone to industrial action and the Cambrian dated 17 Jan 1879 reported that at Pwll Saints Colliery, Fforestfach, 300 hands returned to work after strike over wage cut.

By 1880 it was owned by the Worcester Coal Co., and from the Inspector of Mines listing in 1896, there were 78 men employed producing Manufacturing and Coking coal, and Fireclay. At the time the owner was Phillip Richard of Swansea. The colliery closed in 1898.[11]

OLD WEIGFACH COLLIERY, FFORESTFACH

Situated to the south of Worcester colliery, the old Weigfach colliery was sunk in the early 1840s and purchased by Thomas Stick in 1844. The colliery was sold again in 1849 to Ebenezer Davies and from around 1851 Henry Tregaskis, a local coal merchant, was selling house coal from Weigfach colliery. An advertisement in the Cambrian dated June 1856 stated "Weigfach Colliery & Cwmbach Colliery near Swansea Plant for sale", so it appears that the Old Weigfach closed in that year. Thomas Glasbrook (the brother of John) developed the New Weigfach colliery which struck the rich bituminous seam (Penvilian) at a depth of 100 yards in 1870. The pit was also known as the 'New Worcester' and worked in conjunction with the Worcester pit. In 1874 Weigfach colliery began supplying coal to the Landore Steel Company.[12]

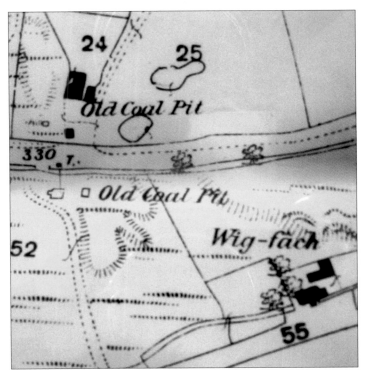

(Plate 5) 1879 O.S. Map showing site of the Old Weig-Fach Colliery which was situated close to the local farm of that name. SS 628950 Courtesy O.H.M.S.

However, a tragic explosion occurred there on the 9 March 1877 killing 18 of the 40 men working, many of whom had large young families:

- Abraham Bevan, Overman, 48 years
- Isaac Williams, Collier, 30 years
- David Davies, Collier, 30 years
- John Davies, Trammer, 16 years
- David Williams, Collier, 33 years
- William Williams, Trammer, 20 years
- Thomas Thomas, Collier, 46 years
- John Morris, unknown
- John Griffiths, Collier, 29 years
- Evan Davies, 29 years
- David Anthony, Collier, 24 years
- Henry Jones, Labourer, 27 years
- David Davies, Fireman, 31 years
- Robert Howells, Trammer, 15 years
- Charles Cooper, Collier, 23 years
- John Prosser, Collier, 56 years
- William Mathews, Trammer, 21 years
- David Thomas (No. 2) Collier, 37 years.

Seven others suffered from the firedamp, but recovered.[13]

The Cambrian reported the accident on 9 March 1877:

"… It is only right to add that this is the first explosion which has occurred in this colliery. It is stated to be exceedingly well ventilated upon the "fan principle" – Mr Thomas Glasbrook, the manager is "well-known" as a most "able and careful manager" and the cause of this sad calamity is at present a mystery and probably will ever so remain, as those who could give any account thereof are killed. Fortunately the full force of the explosion seems to be confined to the Great Slant, or the sacrifice of life would have been far greater. The colliery has been somewhat damaged, but not to the extent that was first supposed. Later on the whole of the 18 bodies were recovered. Mr

Wales, the Government Inspector found upon inspection the blast had produced so little affect on the stability of the workings that it was difficult the actual spot where it had occurred. Having gone through the works he was unable to find any gas except in one working place, where the brattice tubing had been blown down and destroyed. Three or four of the poor fellows killed were slightly burnt by the explosion, but the whole of the deaths were certified by the medical officer to have been caused by after-damp.

We have been informed on reliable authority on examination of the book containing a record of the state of the pit for a considerable period of time past, that the workings were so free from gas that until recently it was considered unnecessary to use safety lamps. Lately however, these have been employed, and their use has been strictly enjoined and enforced on all the colliers descending the pit.

A lamp with the safety case removed from it was found in the neighbourhood of the explosion, which may tend to account for the awful calamity.

The accident has widowed 15 or 16 women, and left fatherless about 45 children. The sad event has cast quite a gloom over the town of Swansea and the whole surrounding district, and such genuine sympathy is expressed towards those who have been thus suddenly and ruthlessly deprived of their relatives and friends …"(14)

Weigfach colliery later came under the control of Phillip Richard of Swansea and probably closed at the same time as the Worcester colliery in 1898.

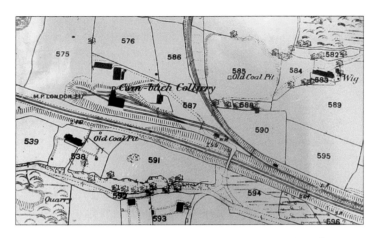

(Plate 6) 1879 O.S. Map showing site of Cwmbach Colliery, Fforestfach. The branch railway line curving northwards to the Worcester and Weig Fach Collieries is from the G.W.R. Cockett Station. SS 628952. Courtesy O.H.M.S.

Opened by W.M. Morris in the 1840s, it was advertised 'to let' with the adjoining Weigfach Colliery in 1851. Applications had to be sent to W.M. Thomas, Millbrook Iron Works (Landore). In 1853 it was run by Elkias Jones & John Jones, after their partnership with William Thomas was dissolved. The colliery was closed in 1856 and their horses and machinery were put up for sale.[15]

It later re-opened, and by 1867 was in the hands of John Thomas, who in 1870 sold it on to T. Glasbrook and Company. In 1869 new machinery was delivered to the colliery and the proprietor treats miners to a picnic. In 1882 it was owned by the Cwmbach Coal Company and worked by T Glasbrook and Co. However, In 1870, an inquest was held over the death of David Evans run over by a tram at Cwmbach Colliery.[16]

By 1882 the mines were worked by the Cwmbach Coal Company. On 19 October 1888, Cwmbach and Saints Pit Collieries, Cockett, Swansea, put up their Machinery and Plant up for sale by a Richard E Hughes. In June 1891 the colliery became abandoned. Surprisingly, in 1923, whilst owned by The Cwmbach Colliery Company, nine men were employed to sink a new shaft. In 1924 the sinking was finally abandoned.[17]

The Colliery worked the Swansea Six-Foot seam (abandoned in June 1991) which had a section of coal 60 inches, dirt 15 inches, coal 12 inches; the Swansea Three-Foot seam (in 1868) which has a section of coal 20 inches, dirt 4 inches, coal 12 inches; and the Swansea Two-Feet seam which had a section of 26 inches.[18]

GORSE COLLIERY, FFORESTFACH

About half a mile to the south of Cwmbach Colliery was the Gorse Colliery, which opened during the early 1850s and was owned by Glasbrook and Richards. It was known locally as Glasbrook's 'El Dorado' because of the volume and quality of bituminous coal mined there.

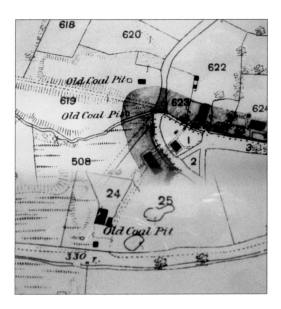

*(Plate 7) 1879 O.S. Map of Site of the Gorse Colliery at Cockett,
which is now occupied by Dillwyn Llewellyn Comprehensive School.
The number of 'Old Coal Pits' marked on the site suggest that
coal extraction had been in in existence for some time. The dark
brush mark is believed the mark the boundary between the Swansea
Borough and Glamorgan County. SS 628946 Courtesy O.H.M.S.*

The first tragedy at the Colliery occurred in August 1855, when
seven year old Mary Price was killed when a tram passed over
her on an incline.[19]

This was followed by an explosion on 9 April 1857. It took
place in a gassy part of the mine where safety lamps were
used.One miner had a safety lamp but removed the cap, and
it was now an open flame. Several of the men remonstrated
him but he refused to replace the cap and an explosion took
place. The dead were named as John Griffiths, aged 35,who
had met the full flame of the blast and was just a charred car-
cass when found, John Mort, 16, and John Knight, 13, both

dying from effects of afterdamp. One young lad of 12 years was found in the same location, but remarkably survived after being brought to his senses.[20]

A report on Gorse Colliery prepared by Thomas Evans, Mines Inspector in 1860 stated:

"This is a small colliery in the neighbourhood of Swansea and it did belong to Messrs Glasbrook and Richards working about 9000 tons of coal per annum. Three lives were lost at these works this year, one from the falling of a loose prop, which had been fixed to support the side of a very dangerous shaft, as well as the roof of the mine. The others lost their life by the falling of a large stone from the roof of the mine at the bottopm of an incline. Only about two years since I had to report the loss of three lives and seven injured from the effects of an explosion consequent on the want of poor management. Since that time I have written to the owners and pointed out the bad state of the colliery with I am sorry to say little good effect. The colliery has now exchanged hands and the present owner Mr. Glasbrook junior has promised to put in a condition fit for men to work in."[21]

The three that died were William Harry, 26 years (Prop of wood fell on him near shaft bottom), John Mathews, 32 years, and David Lloyd, 40 years (Fall of stone in face drift 700 yards to the deep inclination of strata about 40 degrees). There were several other fatalities recorded at this colliery, which was only in production for a dozen years or more. The colliery closed in the mid 1860s.[22]

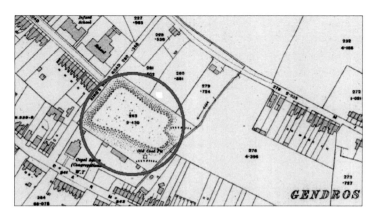

*(Plate 8) 1914 O.S. Map showing site of Site of Gendros &
Charles Colliery (Marked 'Old Coal Pit') The waste spoil tip was
cleared in the 1970s and the site is now a recreational park.
SS 636 952. Courtesy O.H.M.S.*

The Charles Colliery Worked 2 foot, 3 foot and 6 foot veins. It
had no railway nor tramwroad connection to its customers, but
was also worked as a slant where women on donkey carts and
people transporting coal with barrows. The land owner was Sir
Robert Armine Morris (1848–1927) and from 1884 the colliery
was owned by the Charles Brothers and Davies.[23] Its year of closure is not known.

The Colliery was prone to accidents, and on 12 January
1885 an elderly collier from Ravenhill and Deacon of Bethelem
Independent Chapel was killed by large falling stone. Moreover,
on 12 January 1885, Joseph Thomas, 21 years, was working at the
Charles Pit, Gendros when a stone fell on his left leg and broke it.
At the inquest, John Thomas, fireman, stated he had examined
the spot before the accident occurred, and there was no sign of
a loose stone. Dr. Glasbrook Davies said he had attended the deceased, who was suffering from a compound fracture of the left
leg. He was progressing fairly well until Monday, when lockjaw
supervened. The jury returned a verdict of Accidental death.[24]

WIG COLLIERY

Situated off Middle Road near Gendros Crescent Cross. In use 1868–1884. Little is known about the operations of this colliery.[25]

WIG-FAWR Cockett 1884–1898

This colliery, previously discussed, was worked in conjunction with the Weig Fach Colliery and Pwll Sant or "Saint's Pit." On the 8th of March 1877, an unfortunate explosion occurred which killed nineteen of the forty men working underground. Cambrian dated 6 March 1877 reported 19 killed in Explosion at Worcester New Coal Pit, Fforestfach near Swansea, managed by Thomas Glasbrook.

The conversion of the Great Western Railway's broad gauge to standard gauge (4' 8 ½") in 1872, meant that many of the collieries internal rail systems were now compatable with main line traffic and rolling stock could be exchanged. The G.W.R. constructed a spur line from Cockett Station to serve Cwmbach, Weig Fach and Worcester collieries, and so Glasbrook and Richard's railroad became redundant and disappeared.

At this juncture, in the next chapter, we will take a look at the competition for ownership and control of bituminous coal supplies in the Swansea district which brought John Henry Vivian, owner of the largest and most up to date non-ferrous melting enterprises in Europe situated at the Hafod, Swansea, into the local coal mining industry.

CHAPTER XII
BIBLIOGRAPHY AND ILLUSTRATIONS

(1) Swansea History Project, 4 Site Education, Tramroads and Industrial Railways, Paul Reynolds and Gerald Gabb, 2012, p.38 Swansea Refereence Library.

(2) Ibid

(3) Ibid p.41

(4) Ibid

(5) Ibid

(6) Ibid

(7) Ibid p.38

(8) Welsh Coal Mines Forum un-numbered documents

(9) Ibid

(10) Ibid

(11) Ibid

(12) Ibid

(13) Ibid

(14) Ibid

(15) Ibid

(16) Ibid

(17) Ibid

(18) Ibid

(19) Ibid

(20) Ibid

(21) Ibid

(22) Ibid

(23) Ibid

(24) Ibid

(25) Ibid

(Plate 1) 1840 Map of Nathaniel Cameron's planned Swansea to Loughor Railway which followed the line of the Burlais Brook with lines extending from the Pottery to Vivian's Hafod and Morfa Copperworks and Swansea Harbour. Courtesy Glamorgan Archives

(Plate 2) O.S. Map showing routes of Glasbrook and Richard's Cwm Burlais Tramways to Weig Fawr, Gorse, Weig Fach and Worcester Pits. C.1848–1875. SS 639946 Courtesy Swansea Reference Library.Swansea History Project 4. Note the Author has added the RED colliery markers.

(Plate 3) 1879 O.S. Map showing site of Cave Street Tramway Incline (76) and its 'Y' junction with the tramways (73 & 41) leading to the Worcester and Gorse Collieries. SS 641948. Courtesy O.H.M.S.

(Plate 4) 1879 O.S. Map Showing Sites of Worcester and New Weig Fach Collieries, Fforestfach, Swansea. The Tramway shown connected the collieries to the GWR at Cockett Station. SS 628956 Courtesy O.H.M.S.

(Plate 5) 1879 O.S. Map showing site of the Old Wig-Fach Colliery which was situated close to the local farm of that name. SS 628950 Courtesy O.H.M.S.

(Plate 6) 1879 O.S. Map showing site of Cwmbach Colliery, Fforestfach. The branch railway line curving northwards to the Worcester and Weig Fach Collieries is from the G.W.R. Cockett Station. SS 628952 Courtesy O.H.M.S.

(Plate 7) 1879 O.S. Map of Site of the Gorse Colliery at Cockett, which is now occupied by Dillwyn Llewellyn Comprehensive School.The number of 'Old Coal Pits' marked on the site suggest that coal extraction had been in in existence for some time. The dark brush mark is believed the mark the boundary between the Swansea Borough and Glamorgan County. SS 628946 Courtesy O.H.M.S.

(Plate 8) 1914 O.S. Map showing site of Site of Gendros & Charles Colliery (Marked 'Old Coal Pit') The waste spoil tip was cleared in the 1970,s and the site is now a recreational park.SS 636 952. Courtesy O.H.M.S.

CHAPTER XIII

COMPETING FOR THE HOLY GRAIL

Ownership and control of bituminous coal supplies was of even greater importance in the more competitive climate of the mid-nineteenth century. In December 1806, Lockwood formed a new company named the Penvilia Vein Company. The owners transferred the lease of the Five Foot seam under the Beaufort and Pentre estates, canal and tramway rights and the contracts to supply coal to many of the copper companies. Penvilia Vein Co. worked the Pentre Five Foot seam via Penvilia level and the Duke of Beaufort's coal through Clyndu, Treboeth, Hen level y Graig (Park) and Cwm levels. In 1830 the company produced coal from the Beaufort Five Foot seam at the rate of 37,500 tons a year. Interesting was the company's policy to contract out its underground and surface haulage.[1]

By 1811 Lockwood and Co. was intent on remaining in the coal trade, concentrating on shipping through the port of Swansea rather than supplying the local copperworks. In May 1811, after just five years, the Lockwood Co. attempted to surrender its lease on the Pentre pit's Six Foot and Three Foot seams together with all its other mineral estates. Pentre Pit was up for sale. Only the Six Foot and Three Foot seams were on offer, because the Penvilia Vein Co. was still working the Five Foot (Penvilia) Seam.[2]

The Cambrian advertised the two seams and the pit as:

"A capital colliery in an excellent situation for the export trade and the harbour of Swansea. Extending under 400 acres of good free-burning bituminous coal in two veins of Six and Three Foot which have been fully proved, with the engines, erections, machinery and power sufficient for the working and raising of

50,000 chaldrons annually, with rail roads to the shipping places with 17 unexpired prospects."[3]

There is no record of any takers to this advertisement, and John Morris continued to work his Six and Three Foot seams under the Beaufort and Pentre estates. Between 1824-25, Calvert Richard Jones again advertised a new lease for the Six and Three Foot seams under his estate, but there is no record of any interest being shown. Penvilia Vein Company continued to work the Five Foot (Penvilian) seam until 1828. Then once Calvert Jones' property was completely vacant, John Morris stepped in and took a lease extending over all the seams under most of Jones' estate. The lease was to run for 60 years commencing Christmas Day, 1832, although it seems he was in possession of all the coal under the Pentre estate, including Pentre pit, by 1830. The rent was 6 shillings per 10 tons, subject to a dead rent of £1,325 a year.[4]

During this period there was a huge demand for coal from the new smelters near Landore and by 1830, Morris had built an improved railway and self acting plane nearly half-a-mile long connecting Pentre colliery with the Swansea canal. [5]

Indeed, such was the shortage of suitable coal, the rich Penvilia Vein coal was blended with less quality coal to meet the smelters' demands.[6]

In 1811 John Henry Vivian established a large copper smelting works on the banks of the river Tawe, thus ending his interest in the Penclawdd works, which by 1823 had closed. Over the course of the 19th century the Vivians also built an entire settlement for their employees called "Trevivian" or "Vivianstown", which was known as the Hafod. In its day it was one of the largest and most up to date industrial enterprises in Europe, and by the 1840s, Vivian & Sons were the greatest exporters of finished copper in Britain.

When John Henry Vivian died in 1855 his growing industrial empire, centred on the Hafod Copper Smelting Works, was bequeathed in equal portions to his four sons: Henry Hussey (1821–94), William Graham, Arthur Pendarves (1834–1926) and Richard Glyn. The main burden of management fell on the shoulders of

Henry Hussey, the eldest son, who had already guided the fortunes of the firm during the last decade of his father's life. His younger brother, Arthur Pendarves, took responsibility for the Port Talbot side of the business which consisted principally of the Margam Copper Works.[7]

(Plate 1) 1810 Engraving of Hafod Copperworks and Swansea Canal Bridge. Courtesy George Grant Francis, The Smelting of Copper in the Swansea District from the time of Elizabeth to the present day, London, 1881.

Indeed, by the 1830s, Vivian and Sons held a 20% share in the copper market, rising to 27% in the late 1830s. In 1835, John Henry Vivian, John Vivian's son, introduced zinc smelting, and in 1838 the firm took over the smelting works of the English Copper Company at Margam. In 1842, John Vivian's grandson, Henry Hussey Vivian entered the business, and improved the art of zinc smelting by the introduction of new furnaces and helped to develop the firm's collieries.

Vivian and Sons also had interests in the White Rock Copperworks sited on the eastern bank of the river Tawe directly opposite to where the Hafod Works was situated. From 1870 the works produced lead and silver and were operated by William Foster & Co., and Vivian and Sons. From 1874 Vivian and Sons solely operated the works, which is outside the scope of this study.

(Plate 2) Portrait of John Hussey Vivian.
Courtesy Wales on Line. co. uk.

The firm also owned brickworks and the old Forest Spelter Works at Morriston and were colliery proprietors at Mynydd Newydd, Pentrefellen and Pentre. In addition, H.H. Vivian personally owned the Hafod Isha Nickel and Cobalt Works. In 1883 he formed the associated company of H.H. Vivian & Co. Ltd. to take over that works, along with German silver and brass rolling mills at Birmingham.

We will make a short departure at this stage to look at Henry Hussey Vivian's intervention into the religious and educational needs of their workers and families in Vivianstown, by the establishment of St. John's Church and the Hafod Copperworks Schools.

On the west side of Odo Street is the impressive building of St. John's Parish Church. A Vivian benefaction, it was built in 1878–80 in Perpendicular style to designs of architect H. Woodyer of Guildford. The church is constructed of snecked rubble facings with Bath stone dressings under slate roofs. Its plan consisted of twin aisles to nave and east end, with undivided chancel and nave, south organ chamber/vestry, south aisle, west bellcote and south entrance. To the west is evidence at the end of the south aisle for a tower that was never built. Stained glass included work by A.K.Nicholson (1928). The design of the church was intended to incorporate the style of the south aisle of St. Mary's Church, Truro, Cornwall, in which his family are interred, but this was only partly achieved.[8]

(Plate 3) St. John's Church, Odo Street, Hafod.
SS 657946. Courtesy John Ball.

John Henry Vivian approached the architect Henry Woodyer in 1849 for designs for his proposed church at Trevivian (Hafod). At this stage, the Trevivian schools had just been completed, leaving a space to their immediate east at the centre of the development which may well have been the second site intended for the new church. However, "the donor changed his mind"; hence the new church was not built as the centrepiece of the town. It did however dominate a slope looking south-westwards over Cwm Burlais. The Trevivian Anglican church was built a full 35 years after the Vivians had funded schools for the settlement and, when eventually realised, it was only part-funded by the Vivians. There was a depression in the copper industry and the Vivians' plans to build a church in the Cornish style were only partially brought to fruition.[9] After the opening of St. John's, the old parish church in upper High Street, Swansea, was renamed St. Matthew's, and the Trevivian church became the new parish church of St. John-juxta-Swansea.[10]

In 2001 the building was sold off for conversion to social housing, but still retains an area for worship.

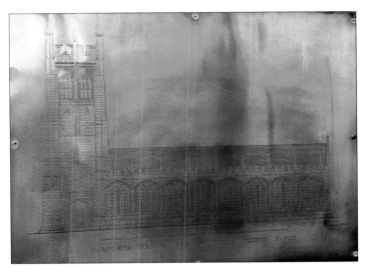

(Plate 4) Polished brass engraving of 'Complete Design for St.John's Church, Hafod.' The large tower, which would have overlooked Cwm Burlais, was never constructed. SS657946. (c) J.P.Thomas. 2 November 2018. Courtesy Rev. Ian Rees.

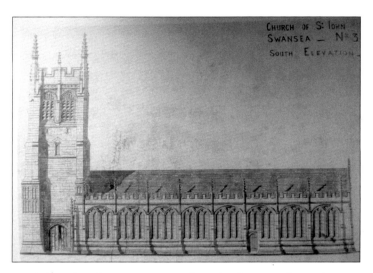

(Plate 5) Architect's Drawing of South Elevation of St. John's Church – No. 3 South Elevation. (c) J.P.Thomas. 2 November 2018. Courtesy Rev. Ian Rees.

(Plate 6) Engraved Copper Memorial Plaque In St. John's Church, Hafod, in memory of Henry Hussey Vivian, 1st Baron Swansea, erected by his sorrowing widow, and contains the words 'Life's race well run. Life's work well done. Life's crown well won. Then comes rest.' SS657946. (c) J.P.Thomas 2 October 2018. Courtesy Rev. Ian Rees.

To the Vivians, education was clearly the path to success. John Vivian and his eldest son, Richard Hussey, had both been partly educated in France. However, the younger son, the 16 year-old John Henry Vivian, went to Germany. In 1803 he enrolled at the famous mining institute of the University od Freiburg where he studied minerology, geology, chemistry, metallurgy and mathematics.[11] This combination of academic and practical training could be attributed to John Henry's success as an industrialist and his reputation as a scientist.

J.H.Vivian regarded education as as the key to industrial efficiency and commented that he was 'constantly deeply conscious of the almost complete lack of educational facilities in the Swansea district'. His wife was a tireless supporter in his educational efforts and Mrs Vivian started a small school for 40 girls in the parish of St. John (Hafod area) in 1825.[12]

(Plate 7) Gable End and entrance to Vivian's Hafod Copperworks Schools, close to corner of Odo Street and Vivian Street, Hafod. The building is now used as a Community Centre. SS 657947. 2 November 2018. (c) J.P.Thomas.

(Plate 8) Rear view of Hafod Copperworks Schools, Odo Street, May 1995. Courtesy COFLEIN.

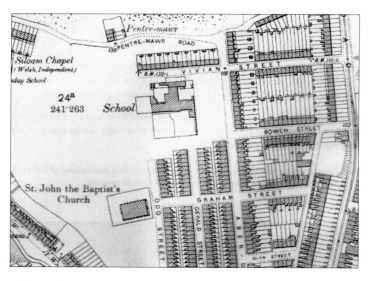

(Plate 9) 1881 O.S. Map of Hafod showing Vivian's School and St. Johns Church. Odo Street has not yet been extended to Pentre-Mawr Road. The school building is extensive with four outside recreational areas. Today, most of the site is residential housing. Courtesy O.H.M.S.

The Hafod Copperworks schools established by the Vivian family at Trevivian, Hafod were among the outstanding works schools of the nineteenth century. Not only were they among the largest schools of their kind numerically and structurally, but they were also organised on an extremely efficient basis, and from their commencement were staffed with fully trained teachers. In addition, they had a comprehensive and large pupil–teacher system, and practically everything in connection with these schools was the subject of the highest praise from the Inspectors of Factories, Inspectors of Schools, and the numerous Commissioners who visited them during the nineteenth century.

However, these were the days before elementary education was made free in 1891. When Sir Henry Hussey Vivian possessed his own Works' Schools, it was once the rule that deductions were to be made from from the wages of those parents whose children attended his schools. The compulsory 'fees' went to support the Work's Schools.[13]

In spite of the depressing industrial environment and meagre salaries, dedicated teachers strove to educate and care for the hundreds of children in their charge. Such a teacher was Mrs. Finley, a headmistress in Mrs. Vivian's Infant School of between three and four hundred pupils. On her death in 1860, the 'Cambrian' reported for the 21st September of that year records:

"We have to regret the death of Mrs. Finley, the devoted schoolmistress of the Hafod (Mrs. Vivian's) Infant School…The wholebody of teachers, both National and British, followed the hearse … scores of the parents, some hundreds of children on foot."(14)

Henry Hussey Vivian was active in Trevivian and its school from an early period: it was especially important after his father entered Parliament in 1832. The schools were taken over by the Swansea School Board in 1898.

We will now return to our work on Hussey Vivian's ownership and control of bituminous coal in the more competitive climate of the mid–nineteenth century.

(Plate 10) Singleton Abbey, Swansea, Home of the Vivian family.
Courtesy 'Wales Online' October 2014.

The next development in coal ownership came in 1839, when the Swansea Coal Company was formed by Vivian & Sons and Williams Foster the two major copper-smelting firms in the district, to take over the assets of the Penvilia Vein Co.

However, on 29 September 1854, Sir John Morris and the Duke of Beaufort leased mines, veins or seams of coal and culm called 6 foot vein, 3 foot vein and 2 foot vein in or under a tract of land called the Fee of Trewyddfa, formerly in tenure or occupation of Sir John Morris. Together with engines and machinery mentioned and specified in schedule: "(ii), their executors, administrators and assigns will yearly and every year during term work, raise or land from and out of mines, veins or seams of coal and culm hereby demised at least 10,666 tons and two thirds of ton of coal and culm to Philip Richard and John Glasbrook, colliery proprietors and copartners, for 42 years."[15] The lease documents are shown below:

(Plate 11) Title of Lease of Coal Mines in the Fee of Trewyddfa in The County of Glamorgan from Henry Charles Fitz Roy, Duke of Beaufort to Phillip Richard and John Glasbrook, both of Swansea, colliery proprietors and copartners dated 2 October 1854. Courtesy West Glamorgan Archives Ref: D/D SB 15/56. (c) J.P.Thomas.

(Plate 12) Indentured Lease Agreement Parchment First Sheet from Duke of Beaufort to Phillip Richard and John Glasbrook dated 2 October 1854. Courtesy West Glamorgan Archives. (c) J.P.Thomas.

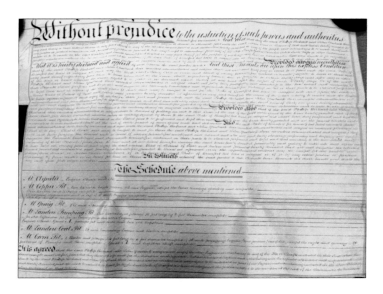

(Plate 13) Second sheet of Deed Parchment with Schedule of Mining Assets contained in Lease. Courtesy West Glamrgan Archives. (c) J.P.Thomas.

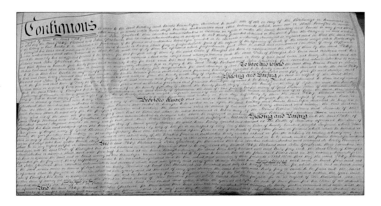

(Plate 14) Third Sheet of Deed Parchment Listing Special Conditions of Lease. Courtesy West Glamorgan Archives. (c) J.P.Thomas.

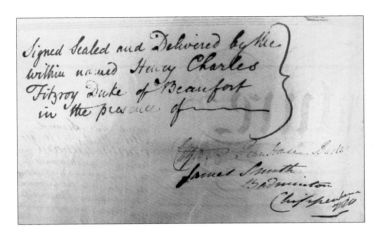

(Plate 15) Signitories of the Lease. Courtesy West Glamorgan Archives. (c) J.P.Thomas.

(Plate 16) Official Seal of Henry Charles Fitz Roy Duke of Beaufort. Courtesy West Glamorgan Archives. (c) J.P.Thomas.

The mines comprised Clyndu, Copper Pit, Craig Pit, Landore (Callands) Pumping Pit, Landore Coal Pit, Cwm Pit and Copper Pit and the lease ensured payment of 9d by way of rent for every ton of 20 hundred weight of coal or culm worked, raised or landed out of ore from 3 veins of coal and culm hereby demised, sum of 2d by way of toll for every ton of coal or culm of 20 hundred weight worked or raised, or yearly further sum of money as will make up full rent of £400 which would have been payable in respect of coal or culm raised, dated 2 Oct 1854.

The 1854 lease to Glasbrook & Richard schedules all the engines that were in place at the various pits on the lease. The entry for Clyndu simply records an engine-house and pit but no engine. In 1854 Glasbrook & Richard acquired the shaft as part of their lease of coal under the fee of Trewyddfa.

The lease endorsed a licence to demise by way of underlease for 24 years, 31 Dec 1872, (i) to (ii) to Henry Hussey Vivian and William Graham Vivian, their executors, administrators and assigns. So much of 3 foot mine, vein or seam of coal and culm demised by within written indenture of lease as lies to west of Cwm Pit fault (Brynhyfryd). Interestingly the assets of the Clyndu mine, apart from the 'Fiery' engine house and pit, make no mention of the underground navigational canal.

However, John H.Vivian died in 1855 followed by Michael Williams in 1858. They were succeeded by Henry. H. Vivian and John Michael Williams. In June 1863, the company dissolved and most of the collieries were allocated to the Vivian family, who believed that regular bituminous coal supplies to their smelting enterprises depended on running their own pits. Indeed they worked their own coal until the end of their business existence in the 1920's.Williams Foster disposed of their last coal interest to John Glasbrook in 1870. There was a belief it was better to buy coal from independent suppliers.[16]

John Morris continued to work all the seams under the Pentre estate until March 1843, when he assigned the Five Foot (Penvilian) seams, including Penvilia level, to the Swansea Coal Co. He retained the Six and Three Foot seams below it and continued to work them through Pentre Pit.[17]

The mining enterprise acquired by the Swansea Coal Co. in 1837 was run down and the existing pits and levels close to exhaustion. These included Callands, Cathelid, Clyndu, Cwm Level, Pentre, Pentrepoeth, and Tircanol. Production in 1842 was down to 28,500 tonnes a year. One of their first tasks therefore was to sink two big new pits, Mynydd Newydd (SS 6388

9649) and Pentrefelen (SS6573 9910). Both were to be connected by a standard railway gauge incline: Mynydd Newydd to the Landore canal wharf for shipment to the Hafod and Morfa works, and Pentrefelen to the Swansea Canal wharf at Tircanol for shipment to local smelters and the port of Swansea.

The Swansea Coal Co. was dissolved in 1863 and its assets divided between the two partners, Vivian & Sons and Williams Foster. The Vivians took over the collieries at Pentre, Cwm Level, Callands, Cathelid (Cwm Clydach) Mynydd Newydd and Pentrefelen; Mynydd Newydd had first yielded coal in 1843, followed by Pentrefelen in 1844.

Interestingly, in 1883 the Cwmfelin Tinplate Company was created by Edward Rice Daniel and his brother-in-law John Jones Jenkins two well known public figures in Swansea. The works was located in the centre of Cwmbwrla and comprised of three blast furnaces coupled with numerous smaller annealing furnaces used in the manufacture of tinplate. An uninterrupted supply of fuel was required so the company opened collieries at Cefyngyfelch (1887) and Tirdonkin (1904), the latter being linked by a mineral railway from Cefngyfelach to Cwmfelin with links to the Great Western Railway. Cefngyfelach was never a large colliery and was abandoned c. 1911, while Tirdonkin survived until 1928 when it fell victim to flooding as was the case with other collieries in the Swansea district.

(The company's venture into coal mining is discussed in Chapter XV)

By 1926, Mynydd Newydd was the only productive pit still owned by the Vivians. The remainder had been either sold or closed. They still owned Calland pumping pit which was essential to preventing flooding and this was included in the deal when the Vivians sold the pit in 1926 to a local syndicate, the Mynydd Newydd Colliery Company Ltd., which had a capital of £10,000 and was composed of colliery officials and local gentlemen.[18]

Demand for non-ferrous metals rose in the 1880s and 1890s as copper was used in the generation and transmission of electricity, which ensured the growth of Vivian and Sons. They secured their own ore supplies and invested in mining, but they mostly turned out to be failures. In the 1890s–1900s, traditional smelting companies such as Vivian and Sons suffered as competition from companies working with their own sources of ore supply. Vivian and Sons became a limited company in 1914, and although they made large profits during World War I, they suffered heavy losses afterwards in the post war depression.

By the mid–1870s, the Vivian & Sons undertaking at Hafod consisted of six works: Hafod Alkali Works, Hafod Copper Mills, Hafod Copper Works, Hafod Iron Foundry, Hafod Phosphate Works, and Hafod Silver Works. The firm also owned brick works and the old Forest Spelter Works at Morriston; were colliery proprietors at Mynydd Newydd, Pentrefellen and Pentre; and had their own shipping offices at 6 Cambrian Place, Swansea. In addition, H.H. Vivian personally owned the Hafod Isha Nickel and Cobalt Works. In 1883 he formed the associated company of H.H. Vivian & Co. Ltd. to take over that works, along with German silver and brass rolling mills at Birmingham.

The main output from the Hafod works at the time were copper ingots which were used locally, or exported. The following picture shows copper ingots manufactured by Vivian & Sons recovered from the wreck of S.S. Benjamain in 1890. The ship was outward bound from Swansea for Treport, north east France, with a 'general cargo', struck rocks of Lundy in fog and was wrecked at Oxwich Bay, Gower on 29 March 1890, with no loss of life. The cargo contained about 20 tonnes of copper ingots marked "V & S": the dimensions of the ingots were length 295mm, width 70mm, height 70mm.[19]

(Plate 17) Vivian & Sons Copper Ingots recovered from wreck of S.S. Benamain, 1890. Courtesy National Museum Wales Collections. Note the V & S trade mark moulded into the ingots.

The Hafod works were also active in producing rolled copper sheet, which was in great demand from the Admiralty for lining their warships with copper sheathing to prevent barnacles clustering on their wooden hulks, thereby increasing their speed and manoeverability. This was apparent in the Battle of Trafalgar near Cadiz, Spain on 21 October 1805, when the English Fleet, including HMS Victory, outran the combined French and Spanish fleet. HMS Victory's Wooden hull was sheathed in copper manufactured at Vivian & Sons Hafod Works.

(Plate 18) Copper sheathing removed from H.M.S. Victory during renovation bearing the Vivian & Sons Swansea 380Z manufacturing stamp. Note the copper nail used to secure the sheathing to the ship's wooden hull. Courtesy HMS Victory Museum, Portsmouth.

(Plate 19) 1900's view of Vivian & Sons plate and sheet metal rolling mill. Note the large steam powered flywheels for driving the rollers. In the foreground are slabs of copper plate awaiting to be rolled into copper sheet. Courtesy Swansea Museum Collection.

In the 1870s Swansea was far ahead of any port in the Bristol Channel, including Bristol, in respect of tonnage registered. Ore from Cornwall was superseded by far richer deposits discovered on the west coast of South America.

The copper ore was now shipped chiefly from the Chilian ports of Valperiso, Caldera, Lota, Autofagasta, Tocopilla and a number of others. It is in this connection with the trade to and from Swansea to the Chilian ports that the name "Copper-ore Cape Horner" is derived. The shipping passage from Swansea to these ports and vice versa involved doubling Cape Horn with its tremendous gales and headless head-winds.[20]

It became apparent in the mid-1880s that it was more economical to smelt ores at the mines in Chile and elsewhere at source, rather than ship them to Swansea. This situation led to the gradual cessation of copper smelting in the Swansea area. No longer necessary to bring the ore to Swansea for refining, one by one the Welsh copper works closed and the chemical industry which was linked with copper-smelting also declined. Moreover, the fabrication of copper had never become established in the Swansea area but had been carried out in London and Birmingham so that with the collapse of copper-smelting, Swansea's stake in the copper industry was lost, apart from two or three works in which sheet and wire production took place. Important though the discovery of new sources of ore and the development of smelting overseas were, a major factor in the decline of smelting in south Wales was the monopolistic practices followed by the industrialists there. By combining to keep up the prices of manufactured copper and to drive down the prices of imported ore, they encouraged ore producers to set up their own smelting works.

In 1924, Vivian and Sons amalgamated with the other major copper smelting firms in Swansea, Williams Foster and Company and Pascoe Grenfell and Sons Limited, to form British Copper Manufacturers' Limited. In the same year Pentre pit ceased operations and the responsibility for pumping at Calland's pit reverted to Vivian and Sons. The company subsequently sold their one surviving colliery, Mynydd Newydd, together with Calland's Pit in 1926, to a local syndicate, the Mynydd Newydd Colliery Company Ltd., which had a capital of £10,000 and was composed of colliery officials and local gentlemen.[21]

The new company was unable to meet the costs of pumping at Callands on its own and sought the assistance of other colliery owners whose mine workings were drained by Callands. The Mynydd Newydd Colliery Company took over from Vivian and Sons in July 1926 and the owners kept on pumping for a time, but eventually ceased. As a result, water levels started rise in the entire district, and most of the Swansea district's collieries were forced to close.

However, in 1837, William Crawford took out a patent for galvanising iron, i.e., coating iron sheets with a thin layer of zinc by dipping them, cleaned by acid, into a bath of molten zinc. Sheets of galvanized corrugated iron were seen to be exciting and glamorous. The concept of adding rigidity to iron sheets not only allowed for the construction of wide-span roofs without the need for cumbersome load bearing walls, but also for them to look new in a built environment dominated by stone and timber. The silvery reflective material was a sign of progress and success of industry. Although uncertain, the first use of galvanized corrugated iron is believed to be for the Navy at Pembroke Docks, Wales in 1844. By 1850, the British galvanising industry was using 10,000 tons of zinc a year and the familiar sheets of 'corrugated iron' were being shipped all over the world.[22]

Though copper waned, Swansea retained an interest in non-ferrous metal production. In the 1860s two erstwhile copper works, the Old Forest (Morriston) and the Upper Bank (Landore) were converted into spelter works and spelter manufacture flourished at the Landore works before it was taken over by Siemen in 1868. New spelter works were built at Port Tennant, Llansamlet and Landore, all in the immediate neighbourhood of Swansea, between 1870 and 1913. At the latter date there were seven zinc-smelting works in active production.

(Plate 20) Former Landore Silver and Spelter (Zinc) Works, Landore, Swansea c.1950. The site was used by William Siemens as an experimental plant when he was developing the open hearth method of steel production. A battery of experimental furnace stacks can be seen behind the chimney stack. Courtesy Swansea Museum Collection.

These new uses for the metal were largely responsible for the expansion of the spelter industry, but their effect was not apparent till the latter part of the century. The Vivians had erected Spelter Works in 1835. In 1868 Mr. Hussey Vivian bought the Old Forest Copper Works and converted them into Spelter Works. It was at this time that the decline in the Copper Trade set in, and copper works were being converted for zinc ore smelting. Although outside the scope of this study, it is worth mentioning that the Upper Bank Works were converted by the Grenfells from copper to zinc production, Messrs. Shackleford and Ford at the Crown Works, Port Tennant, succeeded by Messrs. Richardson and Co, who founded the English Crown Spelter Co., Ltd., in 1883, and Messrs. Dillwyn and Co. at the Llansamlet Works.

In 1947, British Copper Manufacturers' Limited. was taken over by Yorkshire Imperial Metals Limited, a joint company of Yorkshire Metals and Imperial Chemical Industries Limited

(ICI) who then managed the greatly reduced Hafod works until its closure in 1962.

In the next chapter we will look at the operations of the Mynydd Newydd and Pentrefelen Collieries and their advanced coal transportation railroads.

CHAPTER XIII
BIBLIOGRAPHY AND ILLUSTRATIONS

(1) Swansea History Project, 4 Site Education, Tramroads and Industrial Railways, Paul Reynolds and Gerald Gabb, 2012, p.35 Swansea Reference Library.

(2) Treboeth Historical & Pictorial Record.Treboeth Historical Society, 2012. p.129

(3) Ibid p.130

(4) Ibid

(5) Ibid

(6) Ibid p.10

(7) Welsh Journals on Line, Gower, Vol 24 1973,'The Vivian Collieries in 1868 F. G. Cowley, p.80

(8) Images of Wales

(9) Ibid

(10) S. Hughes, Landscapes of the Early Industrial Period In Swansea'p.262.

(11) Ibid p.248

(12) Ibid

(13) N.L. Thomas. The Story of Swansea's Districts and Villages, Parts 1–3, 1959, Guardian Press, p181.

(14) Ibid

(15) Lease of Coal Mines in the Fee of Trewyddfa in The County of Glamorgan from Henry Charles Fitz Roy, Duke of Beaufort to Phillip Richard and John Glasbrook, both of Swansea, colliery proprietors and copartners dated 2 October 1854. West Glamorgan Archives Ref: D/D SB 15/16

(16) Treboeth Historical & Pictorial Record.Treboeth
    Historical Society, 2012 p.108
(17) Ibid p.116
(18) Ibid p.248
(19) National Museum of Wales. Item No. 1994. 170/1
(20) N.L. Thomas. The Story of Swansea's Districts and
    Villages, Parts 1–3, 1959, Guardian Press, p 313.
(21) Treboeth Historical & Pictorial Record, 2012, p.248
(22) Morgannwg, Vol 48, 2004. 'The Early Zinc Works at
    Casllwchwr (Loughor) near Swansea', P.O. Roberts & P.R.
    Reynolds.

(Plate 1) 1810 Engraving of Hafod Copperworks and Swansea
    Canal Bridge. Courtesy George Grant Francis, The
    Smelting of Copper in the Swansea District from the time
    of Elizabeth to the present day. London 1881.
(Plate 2) Portrait of John Hussey Vivian. Courtesy Pinterest
(Plate 3) St. John's Church, Odo Street, Hafod. SS 657946.
    Courtesy John Ball.
(Plate 4) Polished brass engraving of 'Complete Design for
    St.John's Church, Hafod.' The large tower, which would have
    overlooked Cwm Burlais, was never constructed. SS657946.
    J.P.Thomas. 2 November 2018. Courtesy Ian Rees.
(Plate 5) Architect's Drawing of South Elevation of St. John's
    Church – No. 3 South Elevation. J.P.Thomas. 2 November
    2018. Courtesy Ian Rees
(Plate 6) Engraved Copper Memorial Plaque In St. John's
    Church, Hafod, in memory of Henry Hussey Vivian, 1st
    Baron Swansea, erected by his sorrowing widow, and con-
    tains the words 'Life's race well run. Life's work well
    done. Life's crown well won. Then comes rest'. SS657946.
    J.P.Thomas 2 October 2018. Courtesy Ian Rees.
(Plate 7) Gable End and entrance to Vivians Hafod
    Copperworks Schools at corner of Odo treet and Vivian
    Street, Hafod. The building is now used as a Community
    Centre. SS 657947. 2 November 2018. J.P.Thomas

(Plate 8) Rear view of Vivian's Hafod Copperworks Schools, Odo Street. SS 657947. Courtesy COFLEIN May 1995.

(Plate 9) 1881 O.S. Map of Hafod showing Vivian's School and St. Johns Church. Odo Street has not yet been extended to Pentre-Mawr Road. The school building is extensive with four outside recreational areas. Today, most of the site is residential housing. Courtesy O.H.M.S.

(Plate 10) Singleton Abbey, Swansea, Home of the Vivian family. Courtesy ' Wales on Line' October 2014

(Plate 11) Title of Lease of Coal Mines in the Fee of Trewyddfa in The County of Glamorgan from Henry Charles Fitz Roy, Duke of Beaufort to Phillip Richard and John Glasbrook, both of Swansea, colliery proprietors and copartners dated 2 October 1854. Courtesy West Glamorgan Archives Ref: D/D SB 15/56.

(Plate 12) Indentured Lease Agreement Parchment First Sheet from Duke of Beaufort to Phillip Richard and John Glasbrook dated 2 October 1854. Courtesy West Glamorgan Archives Ref: D/D SB 15/56

(Plate 13) Second sheet of Deed Parchment with Schedule of Mining Assets contained in Lease. Courtesy West Glamorgan Archives Ref: D/D SB 15/56

(Plate 14) Third Sheet of Deed Parchment Listing Special Conditions of Lease. Courtesy West Glamorgan Archives Ref: D/D SB 15/56

(Plate 15) Signitories of the Lease. Courtesy West Glamorgan Archives Ref: D/D SB 15/56

(Plate 16) Official Seal of Henry Charles Fitz Roy Duke of Beaufort. Courtesy West Glamorgan Archives Ref: D/D SB 15/56

(Plate 17) Vivian & Sons Copper Ingots recovered from wreck of S.S. Benamain, 1890. Courtesy National Museum Wales Collections.

(Plate 18) Copper sheathing removed from H.M.S. Victory during renovation bearing the Vivian & Sons Swansea

380Z manufacturing stamp. Courtesy HMS Victory Museum, Portsmouth.

(Plate 19) "V & S" Hafod Works copper plate and sheet rolling mill. Note the large steam powered flywheels. Courtesy HMS Victory Museum, Portsmouth.

(Plate 20) Former Landore Silver and Spelter (Zinc) Works, Landore, Swansea. C1950. The site was used by William Siemens as an experimental plant when he was developing the open hearth method of steel production. A battery of experimental furnace stacks can be seen behind the chimney stack. Courtesy Swansea Museum Collection.

CHAPTER XIV

THE MYNYDD NEWYDD AND PENTREFELEN RAILROADS AND THE COLLIERIES THEY SERVED

As discussed previously in Chapter IX, it was in1803 that John Morris II took on a 42 year lease of the Beaufort Six Foot and Three Foot seams, and started to develop Cwm Pit. He installed winding and pumping engines and in around 1805 he relaid an earlier inclined tramway, which had originally been built by Calvert Richard Jones in 1770 to serve his Penvilia Pit (Pwll yr Ayr). Unlike most lines in south Wales at this time, it was an edge railway i.e. with flanges on the wheels of the trams. The technology used on was that of modern-style railway, but using a three-rail system, in which the centre rail was shared by the up and down lines. However the operations at Pwll yr Ayr lasted until 1780 when they were abandoned, with the result that the workings flooded. John Morris bought Townsend's pit and tramway in the early nineteenth century and connected it by a branch-line to the head of the Cwm Level incline and the quay for shipping his coal.

The Swansea Coal Company was formed in 1839 by two major copper smelting houses to take over the Penvilia Vein Company and so ensure their supplies of coal. The business they acquired was run down and the existing pits close to exhaustion. One of their first tasks, therefore, was to sink two big new pits, Mynydd Newydd (SS 6388 9649) and Pentrefelin (SS6573 9910). Both were connected by railroad via a three-rail incline to the Swansea Canal (a wharf at Tircanol) and so to the Hafod and Morfa works via an incline to the Swansea Canal wharf at Landore. Pentrefelin (shown as Pen-Rhiw-Felen Pit on 1879 O.S. Map) started to yield in 1844 and Mynydd Newydd in 1843. The standard gauge (four feet four and half inches) tramroads, which enabled 14 tonne coal wagons to be used on railway company tracks, remained in use until the collieries closed in 1893 and 1932 respectively.[1]

Both were connected by railroad via a three rail incline to the Swansea Canal with wharves at Landore and Tircanol, Morriston for transportation and to the Hafod and Morfa works, via an incline to the Swansea Canal at Landore. Pentrefelen started to yield in 1844 and Mynydd Newydd in 1843. The railroads remained in use until the collieries closed in 1893 and 1932, respectively.[2]

The operating mechanism of the inclines comprised 'sets' of climbing and descending wagons linked by a continuous cable which ran on a series of rollers and guides along the centre of the tracks. At the top of each incline the cable passed through a braking system which controlled the trains' speed. In the middle of each incline, the centre rail divided into a conventional double track layout, so that the trains could pass. The wagons were usually coupled up into trains of four to eight known as sets, with a set-rider riding on a buffer of the first upper wagon (see Plate 2) in each set, whose job was to release the haulage rope linkage from the coupling of the waggon just as the end of the run was reached.

A similar system can be found at the Bowes Inclined Railway near Gateshead, Tyne and Wear. The three-rail inclined system was engineered by George and Robert Stephenson when the Bowes Railway was built linking the Durham Coalfield with the river Tyne near Gateshead.

(Plate 1) View of the Bowes Railway three-rail Incline showing passing loop track arrangement. Courtesy Bowes Railway.

(Plate 2) Bowes Tramway: Set rider on the buffer of an ascending set of trucks. Courtesy Geoff Wright.

(Plate 3) A set of 10 ton coal waggons prepares to descend the Bowes Railway Incline. Note the heavy steel cable from the winding drum attached to the waggon coupling. Courtesy Bowes Railway.

The operation and dangers of these inclines were described by a visitor who journeyed on the Mynydd Newydd Incline in 1899:

"Mynydd Newydd is a colliery belonging to Messrs. Vivian and Sons, and situated on a barren hilltop. My visit was on a tempestuous day, and as I took advantage of the facilities afforded by a surprising and novel means of locomotion, I met with what is conveniently termed "an experience." To save the trudge of a couple of miles up the steep hillside above that grim suburb of Swansea, Landore, the visitor ensconces him-self in one of a string of empty iron coal trains. This suddenly starts up the steep hillside with tremendous velocity, drawn by a steel cable from a winding-drum three quarters of a mile above. About the middle of your wild flight skywards you pass a heavily-laden railway truck coming down the other track. It is your motor, for it is by its weight that you are taken upwards in a series of startling jumps. The cable glides over the big iron pulleys fixed in the middle of the track, sometimes in the groove, sometimes out, grinding and roaring past obstructions, or giving the wheels sudden impulses, and the newcomer feels that his life is not worth a moment's purchase till he finds himself on terra firma at the winding-house above. Here, before a roaring fire, and in the midst of a group of waiting colliers who are going up to the pit's mouth, you await the departure of the next engine pitwards, and being hauled aboard this, you cover the rest of the distance to the pit."(3)

Interestingly, in November 1915, an accident occured on the incline. A set of 4 laden waggons ran out of control on the 1:8 incline, and where it levelled out near Brynhyfryd Square, derailed, and crashed into the rear of the now-closed Brynhyfryd post office situated in Cwm Level Road partly demolishing the building. An investigation showed that frost damage caused the snapping of a bridle chain on one of the waggons. Safety catches on the incline had been sprung open to throw the runaway waggons off the tracks. Fortunately there were no injuries nor deaths.(4)

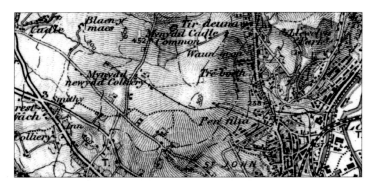

(Plate 4) 1890 O.S. Map showing route of Mynydd Newydd Colliery Railroad to canal wharf at Tyr Glandwr (Landore) and its later connection with the Pentre Pit and GWR Landore Junction Station. Courtesy O.H.M.S.

(Plate 5) The track bed of the former Mynydd Newydd Incline near Brynhyfryd Square now converted to a public footpath. SS 654 958 September 2017 (c) J.P.Thomas.

(Plate 6) 1881 coloured O.S. Map showing the routes of the Pentre Pit (top) and the Mynydd Newydd (bottom) Railroads both having separate coaling wharves on the Swansea Canal. The BLUE coloured tramroad route was originally constructed by Chauncey Townsend to ship coal from Cwm Leval to the Landore river quay via a tunnel. John Morris re-laid the tramway from his Pentre Pit, across the valley floor to join the old Townsend track and incline near Callands Pit. However, Morris replaced the whole line with a modern 3-rail system which could cope with increased coal tonnage.

MYNYDD NEWYDD COLLIERY

When the Swansea Coal Company sunk Mynydd Newydd in 1843, it originally sunk to the Five Foot vein at 130 yards. In 1886 it was taken over by Vivian and Sons. Later the shaft was deepened to the Six Foot seam at 280 yards; it was then connected underground to the Pentre Pit for which it supplied ventilation.[5]

During the 1920s and early 30s, the 6ft, 3ft, and 2ft seams were worked, producing the best house locality. Consumers could easily burn 50% rubbish with it.[6]

However, the roofing and floor of the 5ft (Penvilian) seam were frequently in poor shape, presenting a continual hazard to those cutting this particular vein. The colliers had to contend with what was known as "Pwokin," or swelling of the floor, which had to be cut away almost every day in order to facilitate the smoth running of traffic.

The roof of the 5ft Penvilian seam also suffered from the effects of "Pans" or "Bells,"a very dangerous condition, especially when the roof became exposed. These would slip out without warning and could only be discerned by the experienced miner. When, for example, a collier was sounding his roof and saw indications of coal around the edge, he would realise the existence of a "Pan," and immediately make use of every preparation to place a support through the use of pit props. Next he would hasten to erect a "pair of timber," and lag the roof in quickly. The safety pit prop placed in previously was then withdrawn.[7]

A high number of these occurrences of "Pans" or "Bells" took a heavy toll of life here, as often it was in the 5ft seams of neighbouring mines. At times, even the most knowledgeable of miners sometimes failed to detect the warning signs of a "Pan".[8] Apart from roof falls, fire-damp explosions were the bane of colliers. On May 22 1846, youngsters David Jones, 14 years, David Jones, 14 years, William Lodwick, 12 years, and John David, 17 years, were killed in such an explosion. This tragedy was followed by another explosion on April 02 1869, which claimed the lives of Joseph Mathews, 38 years, Thomas Mathews, 30, and Enoch Lewis, 16 years, who was the son of John Lewis, Pit Fireman.[9]

It was in 1845, when the Colliery had been open for two years, that a group of colliers met to discuss how best they could safeguard the pit and themselves from explosions and other accidents. The group decided that holding prayer meetings in the depth of the earth was the most effective remedy. A chamber 16 yards by 6 yards was excavated out of the 5 foot Penvilian seam. [10] In 1869 a second chamber was built, this time from the 6 foot seam with seating accommodation for about 100 miners.[11]

(Plate 7) Mynydd-Newydd Colliery, Cadle. 1850.
SS 634965. Courtesy OSS Glamorgan XIV 16

Arthur Pendarves Vivian made an inspection of the colliery on March 8th, 1868 and reported:

"Winding shaft about 60–70 fathoms where it strikes the 5 ft. vein – varying in thickness from 5 to 9 ft. in different parts of the colliery, dip 6 in. in the yard-sunk close on the synclinal. The 4 ft. vein which is the next above the 5 ft. is just out of the ground. Next below the 5 ft. is the 6 ft. about 50 fathoms down-on which Padley's, Struves' and the Gorse collieries are sunk. The pumping pit is about 50 yards to the E. and is the downcast. The 5 ft. is the only vein worked and cuts large-roof bad. The 6 ft. has been worked to the rise and will therefore according to new proposal have to be drained from Landore when re-opened. The 4 ft. vein is very high in the measures. Then comes the 5 ft., 6 ft., 3 ft. and a lot of smaller 3 ft. veins until you come to the Hughes vein. The ground to Pennant between this and Wern Pistole Cwm Avon section is very little known. Then comes our Brombill measures-lower still the Morfa measures. By the agreement entered into with Messrs. Williams in Feb. 1863 they retain Tyrcenol in their own hand and we receive as our portion Pentre, Cwm Level, Mynydd Newydd and Pentrefelin, each at the cost of stocks and materials as they stand on the Swansea Coal Co's. books and following sketch of the above collieries is from observations made in going over them with Hussey on February 19th and 20th of the same year."[12]

Interestingly Vivian mentions the Penvilian 5ft seam and its bad roof and the rise in minewater at the 6 ft seam and the need to have it drained from Landore (Callands Pit).

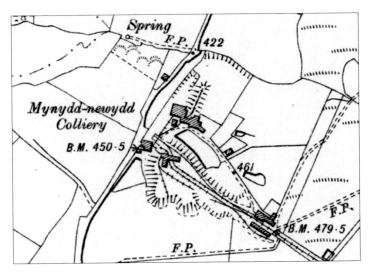

(Plate 8) 1889 O.S. Site Map of Mynydd Newydd Colliery, Cadle. SS 634945. Courtesy O.H.M.S.

Meanwhile, at this point of time, the owners of both the Mynydd Newydd and Pentre collieries were looking at means of cutting back on their coal transportation costs. Having two canal wharves serving two tramways in close proximity to one another did not make economic sense, so it was decided to truncate the Mynydd Newydd railroad at Brynhyfryd Square and construct a spur line along Pentrefelin Terrace to join the Pentre railroad leading to the Swansea canal wharf as shown on the following map:

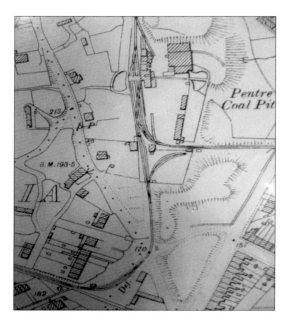

(Plate 9) 1873 O.S. Map showing Mynydd Newydd Railroad truncated at Brynhyfryd Square and re-routed via Pentrefelin Terrace to join the Pentre Colliery Tramway with access to the Swansea canal wharf at Landore. The BLUE line shows the original track route to Tir Glandwr canal wharf which was then abandoned.

Due to the complexity of the 3-rail haulage rope linkage system, sets of coal trucks from Mynydd Colliery would first be directed to the sidings at Pentre Colliery, and then reversed on to the Pentre Railroad for transportation to the wharf. The Swansea canal wharf at Tir Glandwr was then no longer required.

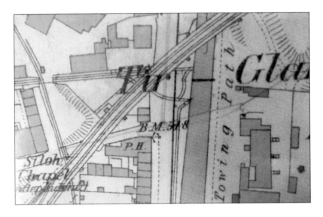

(Plate 10) 1876 coloured O.S. Map showing staithes and sidings of the Mynydd Newydd Colliery Railroad at the Swansea Canal Wharf at Tir Glandwr [Landore]. Courtesy O.H.M.S.

Once both railroads were able to share the use of the tramway and coaling wharf the track section section between Brynhyfryd Square and the canal wharf at Tir Glandwr was closed and lifted.

(Plate 11) Abandoned trackbed of former Mynydd Newydd 3-Rail Railroad running at rear of backyards of houses in Siloh Road, before reaching inclined section to Landore canal wharf. The railway level of the Landore viaduct, which the railroad passed beneath, can be seen in the distance., SS 659958. May 2018. (c) J.P.Thomas.

However, the South Wales Railway was amalgamated with the Great Western Railway in 1863 and the six foot gauge track was converted to the narrower standard gauge in 1873.

At the about same time, the standard Pentre Railroad was re-routed with a spur line via the Millbrook Iron Works to join the Great Western Railway at Landore junction station rather than the canal.

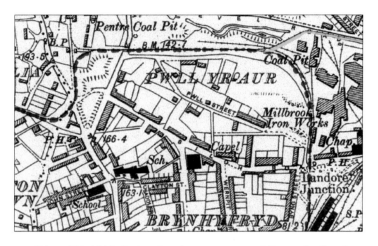

(Plate 12) 1890 O.S. Map showing re-routed Pentre Railroad (RED) to Great Western Railway at Landore Junction. The YELLOW track section to the canal wharf became redundant and was lifted. SS 659956.

(Plate 13) 1930s Aerial Photograph showing re-routed Pentre Railroad connecting with the Great Western Railway sidings at Landore Junction Station, Swansea. The disused incline and trackbed of the Mynydd Newydd Railroad which led to a coaling wharf on the Swansea Canal at Tir-Landwr has been obliterated..The disused Callands' Pit and Cwm Level Road can be seen in the background. SS 659956 Courtesy Aerofilms.

By the 1890's coal traffic from the two pits could be hauled by steam locomotion to sidings at Landore Junction station for distribution by railway.[13]

We will now return to our work on the Mynydd Newydd colliery.

During the ownership of the Mynydd Newydd mine by the Vivians, it was realised how very essential it was to maintain the pumping of water at 'Pwll Calons' (Calland's Pit), Brynhyfryd, situated in the basin. When the Vivians finally gave up Mynydd Newydd, a small company, Watkins & Co., was formed to carry on working the seams of coal which were already exposed.

However, the Company felt that the financial burden of operating the pumping station at Pwll Calons would prove too much for them. Consequently, it was decided to seek the active co-operation of the other local colliery companies and pointed out to them the impending dangers of flooding over a wide area if proprietors failed to band together in maintaining the pumping activities.[14]

In the event, after hearing the report of its delegation, the Mynydd Newydd Company decided they could no longer continue to operate the Pwll Calons (Calland's) pumping station, which was later dismantled. Within months, as anticipated, water began to fill up and rose to such heights that it found a weakness at the spot marked "John Gray's Fault." As a result the water spread into the workings of the new Watkins' concern.

In spite of this setback, the Company managed, for a while longer, to keep it going. Fortunately, there was a "Deep" situated not far from the pit bottom, leading to the water shaft, which contained the early inrush of water and enabled the Company to drive a crossing from the shaft to the deep. The flood waters were then siphoned from the deep to the surface and curtailed the working sections being flooded for several months.[15]

It was a desperate situation, since some 200 men's jobs were at risk. Difficulties began to increase at Mynydd Newydd, so much so that the owner was forced into requesting his men to work the mine for several weeks without wages. This they gallantly agreed to do as a "last stand measure", in the hope of keeping the colliery going until things improved again. However, there was a limit to such sacrifices, and as there were no indications that matters were on the mend, the men met and decided unanimously not to work any further unless they were paid. A delegation respectfully informed company chairman Mr. Watkins of their colleagues decision of "No wages, no work!" On hearing this news he replied: "Gentlemen, I am not worth more than the walking-stick which is holding me up!"[16]

After the first shock of this startling announcement, the delegation then acquainted the proprietor with an emergency plan they had in mind, which was to seize the loaded trucks of coal standing in the siding and share out the stocks among the men as part payment for the wages already lost to them. An astonished delegation soon had this idea squashed, for their proprietor answered with the words: "Do not touch the stocks of coal because I have already mortgaged the lot, and the Law would very soon be upon you."[17]

It was the end of the line for the Company and all concerned; its owner had gambled but failed in the endeavour to sell the coal worked by the miners without payment, and consequently went further into debt. He was unable to recoup some of his losses, and worse still could not pay the monies due to his employees. The miners departed for home after hearing the worst from their delegation at practically the same time as the Official Receiver was phoned for by the proprietor. Under these circumstances the miners involved not only lost their wages but also their individual sets of working tools which averaged between £12 and £15 a set.[18]

It was a bitter and sad ending to mining the Great Penvilian Vein. It was a classic case of "Hope and Heartbreak," which at the time, was impacting on the lives of many miners, particularly those working at the Pentre Pit, Landore, which closed in 1926, and the Copper Pit, Morriston, which closed in 1938.[19]

A legacy of coal mining from both the Mynydd Newydd and Pentrefelen collieries, which supplied Vivian's smelters with the rich Penvilian bituminous coal required to smelt the copper ore, were the vast deposits of waste slag to be found dumped on Hafod tip on the lower Swansea valley floor:

(Plate 14) The original riverside tip of the Hafod Copperworks (1909). The Chimney Stack that had originally released harmful fumes is visible together with a newly built aerial ropeway replacing the earlier tramway still in situate. Courtesy Swansea Museum, Collection.

(Plate 15) 1946 RAF aerial view of Vivian's Hafod Copper Slag Tip. The site has been cleared and is now occupied by Pentrehafod Secondary School. SS 657949. Courtesy RCAHMW.

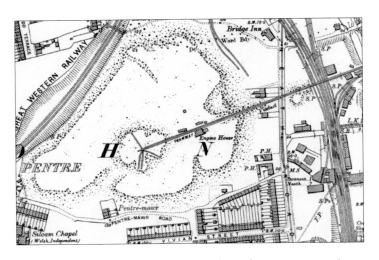

(Plate 16) 1881 O.S.Map showing elevated tramway connecting Hafod copper slag tip with Vivian's copperworks. Courtesy O.H.M.S.O.

In neighbourhoods, like Pentrehafod, the tip shed its slag waste sometimes blocking roadways and almost residents' front doors.

(Plate 17) 1930's View of copper slag waste from Vivian's Hafod Tip over-flowing onto Pentre Mawr Road and Aberdyberthi Street, Hafod. SS 658948. Courtesy RISW.

(Plate 18) View of Pentre Mawr Road and Aberdyberthi Street, Hafod, 1 May 2018. The copper slag from Vivian,s Hafod Tip has been cleared. The area has been landscaped and Pentrehafod Secondary School occupies the site. SS 657948. (c) J.P. Thomas. 1 November 2018.

MYNYDD NEWYDD COLLIERY COMPANY
Limited.

The Companies Act, 1929.

AT an Extraordinary General Meeting of the Members of the above named Company, duly convened, and held at Angel Chambers, York Street, Swansea, on the 3rd day of August, 1932, the following Extraordinary Resolution was duly passed:—

"That it has been proved to the satisfaction of this Meeting that the Company cannot, by reason of its liabilities, continue its business, and that it is advisable to wind up the same, and accordingly that the Company be wound up voluntarily; and that Mr. Thomas Mills, of 22, Wind Street, Swansea, Incorporated Accountant, be and he is hereby appointed Liquidator for the purposes of such winding-up."

(136)   **DAVID WATKINS, Chairman.**

(Plate 19) Mynydd Newydd Colliery Winding Up Notice. Courtesy London Gazette 8 August 1932.

MYNYDD NEWYDD DRIFT MINE

A final attempt was made to work the Five Foot (Penvilian) seam by a new company. The Mynydd Newydd Colliery Company (1933) Ltd worked the Mynydd Newydd drift mine for nine months before rising water forced them to abandon the undertaking in June 1934.

After this venture, W. Craven Llewellyn opened a drift mine at the botton end of Sir John Llewellyn's Penllergare estate at Cadle Mill, presumably driving towards the Five Foot (Penvilian) seam, where there was the danger of a large accumulation of water.

This company was succeeded by the Mynydd Newydd Company (1935) Ltd. In 1935 the drift had to be abandoned and boilers and pumps were installed to cope with the water.

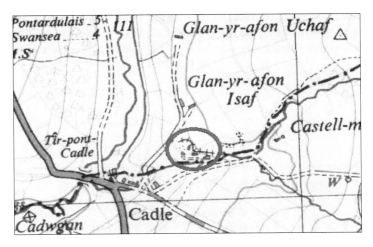

(Plate 20) 1937 O.S. Site Map of Mynydd Newydd Drift Mine. Note the short tramway from the drift mine to the waste spoil tip.

Coal production resumed in 1937 and the slant survived until its closure in 1955.[20] The mine did not have a railway connection and coal was transported by road haulage.

PENTREFELEN (PEN-RHIW-FELEN) RAILROAD

The route of the Pentrefelen standard gauge 3 rail railroad ran from Pentrefelen Colliery to a wharf on the Swansea canal at Tircanol, Morriston. The track followed reasonably level ground from Llangyfelach to Vicarage Road, Morriston, across what is now the Morriston Golf Course, but then encountered a steep incline leading to Tircanol.

(Plate 21) 1880 O.S. Map showing route of Pentrefelen Railroad from Bryn-Whilach and Pentrefelen coal pits to canal wharf at Tircanol. Courtesy O.H.M.S.

On the Pentrefelen railroad was an Engine House and winding drum situated near Llangyfelach to provide haulage to move the laden coal trucks from their collieries to the winding house at the top of the incline at Vicarage Road, where they would descend by gravity to the canal wharf at Tircanol, and in turn raise the empty trucks up the inclne to be returned to their respective collieries. The Pentrefelen and Mynydd–Newydd railroad inclines were self acting and similar in their construction and operation, although 2-holed stone sleeper blocks were used in preference to wooden supports.

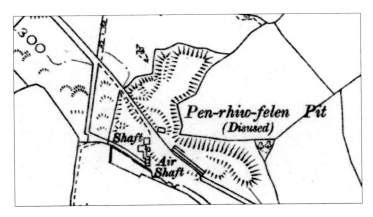

(Plate 22) 1879 O.S. Site Map of Pen-rhiw-felen (Pentrefelen) Colliery, near Morriston. SS 657 991. Courtesy O.H.M.S.

(Plate 23) Aerial view of former Pentrefelen Railroad, now farmland track, near Brynwhilach., Llangyfelach. SS 654994 October 2017 Courtesy Maps.nls.uk/os/25 inch, England & Wales.

Connected to the railroad by means of a short tramway was Brynwhilach Colliery:

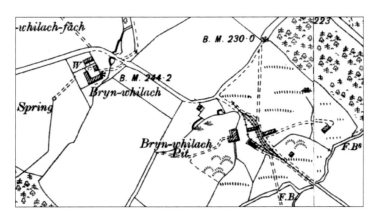

(Plate 24) 1869 O.S. Site Map of Bryn-whilach Colliery, near Morriston. SS 647001 Courtesy O.H.M.S.

Bryn Willach at SS 647001 worked the Two Feet and Four Feet seams and was listed from 1869 to 1887, when it was abandoned. It was advertised for sale the following year, without success. The owner was H. H. Vivian throughout this period, but an abortive company, under the name Swansea & Neath Collieries Co. Ltd. was registered on 2.11.1873 with a view to purchasing the colliery. This company, though registered, was never actually formed, but fell through for lack of shareholders. The mine was connected by tramway to the railroad leading from Pentrefelin Colliery to the Swansea Canal.[21]

Abergelli at SS 651018 worked the Four Feet and Graigola (also known as the Brynwhilach) seams and was listed from 1926 to 1960. The owner up to nationalisation was the Graigola Merthyr Co. Ltd. and it was worked in association with Clydach Merthyr. As at 15.12.1947, Abergelli was detailed as a cross measure drift to the Four Feet seam at 180 yards, thence the Graigola seam at 530 yards. The coal was banked at Clydach Merthyr. The Brynwhilach seam was abandoned 20.4.1953 and the Swansea Four Feet seam on 13.4.1960.[22]

(Plate 25) Remains of Pentrefelen Railroad Embankment at lower Morriston Golf Course SS 663989 September 2017. (c) J.P.Thomas.

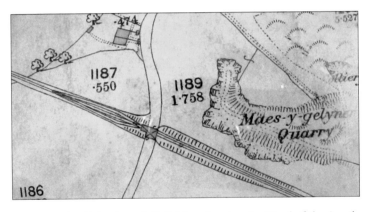

(Plate 26) 1879 coloured O.S.Map showing the Head of the 3-rail Pentrefelen Railroad Incline at Vicarage Road, Morriston, where a winding engine house was situated.
SS 666987. Courtesy O.H.M.S.

(Plate 27) Gem Road, Morriston: Route of the Pentrefelin Railroad and Incline which ran from the canal wharves at Sway Road, Ticanol, up an escarpment to Vicarage Road, and then on to Pentrefelin and Brynwhilach Collieries near Llangyfelach. Interestingly the garden wall of the far property is constructed of black slag bricks and and coping stones, a by-product of copper smelting. SS 671986. (c) J.P.Thomas. April 2017.

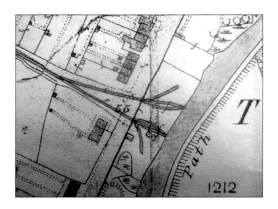

(Plate 28) 1879 O.S. Map showing Pentrefelen Incline Coaling Staithes and Sidings at Swansea Canal, Tircanol, Morriston. Lidl's Store currently occupies this site. SS 671986. Courtesy O.H.M.S.

258

Following the completion of the Great Western Railway Branch Line to Morriston (Pentrefelen) in 1881, a new standard gauge railroad bridge was built crossing the Swansea Canal at Tircanol, enabling coal waggons to be taken by train directly to the copper smelting works or Swansea Docks for export, thus eliminating the use of the canal, coal staithes and wharf, which was also the case with the Mynydd Newydd Railroad.

(Plate 29) Pentrefelen Railroad Canal Bridge at Tircanol, Morriston, where there were G.W.R. coal storage sidings. Lidl's supermarket now occupies this site. The Tutor-styled building in the background was known as the mission hall and became a temporary Sunday School for Saint Teilo's Church in around 1925. SS 672984 Courtesy. Gareth Mills Swansea Docks Collection.

However, mining safety was still an issue and colliery explosions were still occurring in Swansea district during the mid-19th century. On 27th December, 1844, an explosion took place at the Pentrefelen Colliery, Morriston. 'The Cambrian' and the 'Carlisle Patriot' newpapers reported:

"COLLIERY EXPLOSION IN WALES"

"Soon after the workmen entered the Pentrefelen Colliery, the property of the Swansea Coal Company, situated near Morriston, on Monday week, they were alarmed by the explosion of foul air in one of the headings, ignited by a collier named Thomas JAMES, who was most severely burnt.

The workmen immediately proceeded from all part of the pit to the scene of the lamentable occurrence, where they found the three lifeless bodies of John HOPKIN, aged 20, Matthew FISHER, aged 20, both of whom were unmarried, and Thomas MORGAN, a boy ten years of age, who had been most shockingly disfigured – his head having been detached from his body by the violent concussion of air consequent upon the explosion.

An inquest on the bodies of the sufferers was held at the Crown Public House, Morriston, on Wednesday, when several witnesses were examined, and the jury returned a verdict of "accidental death," with an opinion, "that had the fan been worked during Sunday night, or early on Monday morning, the explosion would not have occurred – that there is blame attached to the overman for not having seen that the pit was properly cleared, and for not having employed a person sufficiently strong to work at the fan."[23]

The Pentrefelen railroad closed in 1893 whilst the Mynydd Newydd continued operations until 1932.

In the next chapter we be looking at the Cwmfelin Steel and Tinplate Co. Ltd.'s venture into coalmining at its Cefngyfelach and Tirdonkin collieries.

CHAPTER XIV
BIBLIOGRAPHY AND ILLUSTRATIONS

(1) S. Hughes and Paul Reynolds. Industrial Archaeology of the Swansea Region. A.I.A., 1988, p.38.

(2) Ibid.

(3) A visit to Mynydd Newydd by W. Walford Moore 1899 Fforestfach History un-numbered page.

(4) Treboeth Historical & Pictorial Record.Treboeth Historical Society, 2012. P.115

(5) Welsh Coal Mines Forum un-numbered page

(6) N.L. Thomas. The Story of Swansea's Districts and Villages, Parts 1–3, 1969, Guardian Press, p181.

(7) Ibid, p.171.

(8) Ibid, p.182.

(9) Welsh Coal Mines Forum, un-numbered page

(10) Treboeth Historical & Pictorial Record.Treboeth Historical Society, 2012. P.118

(11) Ibid, p.121.

(12) (Welsh Journals on Line, Gower, Vol 24 1973,'The Vivian Collieries in 1868 F. G. Cowley, p.80

(13)Swansea History Project, 4 Site Education, Tramroads and Industrial Railways, Paul Reynolds and Gerald Gabb, 2012, p.38 Swansea Reference Library

(14) N.L. Thomas. The Story of Swansea's Districts and Villages, Parts 1–3, 1969, Guardian Press, p181.

(15) Ibid. p.182

(16) Ibid, p183

(17) Ibid.

(18) Ibid.

(19) Ibid.

(20) Treboeth Historical & Pictorial Record.Treboeth Historical Society, 2012. P.117.

(21) Welsh Coal Mines Forum. un-numbered page.

(22) Ibid

(23) Cambrian 28 December 1844.

(Plate 1) View of the Bowes Railway three-rail Incline showing passing loop track arrangement. Courtesy Bowes Railway.

(Plate 2) Bowes Tramway: Set rider on the buffer of an ascending set of trucks. Courtesy Geoff Wright. Uphill and Downhill: Inclined Planes. Gwilli Railway Messenger, No.19, Winter 2011, pp 35–37

(Plate 3) A set of 10 ton coal waggons prepares to descend the Bowes Railway Incline. Note the heavy steel cable from the winding drum attached to the waggon coupling. Courtesy Bowes Railway.

(Plate 4) 1890 O.S. Map showing route of Mynydd Newydd Colliery Railroad to canal wharf at Tyr Glandwr (Landore) and its later connection with the Pentre Pit and GWR Landore Junction Station. Courtesy O.H.M.S.

(Plate 5) The track bed of the former Mynydd Newydd Incline near Brynhyfryd Square now converted to a public footpath. SS 654 958 September 2017.

(Plate 6) 1881 coloured O.S. Map showing the routes of the Pentre Pit and the Mynydd Newydd Railroads both having separate coaling wharves on the Swansea Canal.

(Plate 7) Mynydd–Newydd Colliery, Cadle. 1850. SS 634965 Courtesy Google Images.

(Plate 8) 1889 O.S. Site Map of Mynydd Newydd Colliery, Cadle. SS 634945 Courtesy O.H.M.S.

(Plate 9) 1873 O.S. Map showing Mynydd Newydd Railroad truncated at Brynhyfryd Square and re-routed via Pentrefelin Terrace to join the Pentre Colliery Tramway with access to the Swansea canal wharf at Landore.

(Plate 10) 1876 coloured O.S. Map showing staithes and sidings of the Mynydd Newydd Colliery Railroad at the Swansea Canal Wharf at Tir Glandwr [Landore]

(Plate 11) Abandoned trackbed of former Mynydd Newydd 3-Rail Railroad running at rear of backyards of houses in Siloh Road, before reaching inclined section to Tir Glandwr canal wharf.

(Plate 12) 1890 O.S. Map showing re-routed Pentre Railroad (RED) to Great Western Railway at Landore Junction. SS 659956

(Plate 13) 1930's Aerial Photograph showing re-routed Pentre Railroad connecting with the Great Western Railway sidings at Landore Junction Station, Swansea.

(Plate 14) The original riverside tip of the Hafod Copperworks (1909). The Chimney Stack that had originally released harmful fumes is visible together with a newly built aerial ropeway replacing the earlier tramway still in situate. Courtesy Swansea Museum, Collection.

(Plate 15) 1946 RAF aerial view of Vivian's Hafod Copper Slag Tip. The site has been cleared and is now occupied by Pentrehafod Secondary School. SS 657949. Courtesy RCAHMW.

(Plate 16) 1881 O.S.Map showing elevated tramway connecting Hafod copper slag tip with Vivian's copperworks. Courtesy O.H.M.S.O.

(Plate 17) 1930's View of copper slag waste from Vivian's Hafod Tip over-flowing onto Pentre Mawr Road and Aberdyberthi Street, Hafod. SS 658948. Courtesy RISW.

(Plate 18) View of Pentre Mawr Road and Aberdyberthi Street, Hafod, 1 May 2018. The copper slag from Vivian,s Hafod Tip has been cleared. The area has been landscaped and Pentrehafod Secondary School occupies the site. SS 657948. (c) J.P. Thomas. 1 November 2018.

(Plate 19) Mynydd Newydd Colliery Winding Up Notice. Courtesy London Gazette 8 August 1932.

(Plate 20) 1937 O.S. Site Map of Myydd Newydd Drift Mine.

(Plate 21) 1880 O.S. Map showing route of Pentrefelen Railroad from Bryn-wwhilach and Pentrefelen coal pits to canal wharf at Tircanol.

(Plate 22) 1879 O.S. Site Map of Pen-rhiw-felen (Pentrefelen) Pit, near Morriston. Courtesy O.H.M.S.

(Plate 23) Aerial view of former Pentrefelen Railroad, now farmland track, near Brynwhilach., Llangyfelach.

(Plate 24) 1869 O.S. Site Map of Bryn-whilach Pit, near Morriston.

(Plate 25) Remains of Pentrefelen Railroad Embankment at lower Morriston Golf Course.

(Plate 26) 1879 coloured O.S.Map showing the Head of the 3-rail Pentrefelen Railroad Incline at Vicarage Road, Morriston, where a winding engine house was situated.

(Plate 27) Gem Road, Morriston: Route of the Pentrefelin Railroad and Incline which ran from the canal wharves at Sway Road, Ticanol, up an escarpment to Vicarage Road, and then on to Pentrefelin and Brynwhilach Collieries near Llangyfelach.

(Plate 28) 1879 O.S. Map showing Pentrefelen Incline Coaling Staithes and Sidings at Swansea Canal, Tircanol, Morriston.

(Plate 29) Pentrefelen Railroad Canal Bridge at Tircanol, Morriston.

CHAPTER XV

A TALE OF TWO COLLIERIES – THE CWMFELIN STEEL AND TINPLATE CO. LTD.'S VENTURE INTO COALMINING AT ITS CEFNGYFELACH AND TIRDONKIN COLLIERIES

Coal had been mined in the parish of Llangyfelach since the thirteenth century and subsequent landowners were well aware of the potential wealth to be won from the underlying coal measures – some of which outcropped to permit exploitation from simple bell-pits – in acquiring additions to their estates. Gryffydd Price's colliery interests were relatively extensive and profitable, but it was left to Sir John Talbot Dillwyn Llewelyn, taking advantage of the expanding demand for smokeless steam coal locally and for export, to actually open mines on Penllergare land. These were mainly Cefngyfelach (SS 647979), Cadle (SS 627972) and Tirdonkin (SS (SS634983).[1]

The Price family had lived in Penllegaer House for more than two hundred years and had been mining coal since the 1660s. Thomas Price and his son Gryffydd had been in serious conflict with John Morris of Clasemont and the Duke of Beaufort in the mid-1700s over mineral rights on Graig Trewydda resulting in the deaths of six miners working in the Clyndu Level Colliery, Morriston (see Chapter II). Gryffydd Price, the last of the family line, left the house to his cousin John Llewellyn of Ynysygerwn in his will dated 1783.

(Plate 1) 1904 View of Penllegaer House. Residence of Sir John Dillwyn-Llewelyn. The building was demolished in 1961. SS 623990. Courtesy COFFEIN.

Between 1843 and 1886 the Swansea Coal Co., and later Vivian & Sons had a lease of all the coal seams under Cefngyfelach apart from the Six Foot. They worked the Five Foot (Penvillian) through Clyndu Level Colliery, Morriston, where the workings had reached Llangyfelach where a geological fault was discovered. John Glasbrook had a lease of the Six FoFoot from 1883 to 1896 or later, and worked it through Cwm Pit, Brynhyfryd.[2]

The Cwmfelin Steel and Tinplate Works was situated in the centre of Cwmbwrla, Swansea, abounded by Carmarthen Road, Ysgubor Fach Street, Llangyfelach Road and the Great Western Railway main line from Swansea to west Wales. These days the site is occupied by a housing estate.

(Plate 2) 1946 RAF Aerial View of Cwmfelin Steel and Tinplate Works, Cwmbwrla. Courtesy West Glamorgan Archives.

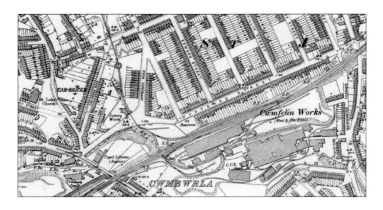

(Plate 3) 1916 O.S. site map of Cwmfelin Steel and Tinplate Works. The RED marker shows the Cefngyfelach Colliery railway passing through Cwmbwrla beginning its ascent to the mine. It can be seen the line had connections with both the works and the Great Western Railway main line. Courtesy O.H.M.S.

(Plate 4) 1800's Street Scene in Llangyfelach Road adjacent to Cwmfelin Tinplate Works, Cwmbwrla. Note the battery of annealing furnace stacks. SS 653947. Courtesy Joel Nicholas.

(Plate 5) 1980's View of Cwmfelin Tinplate Works at junction of Ysgubor Fach Street and Llangyfelach Road.The buildng is in disrepair and the battery of annealing furnace stacks has been demolished. SS 653947. Courtesy Peter Bailey.

In about 1860, Edward Rice Daniel became a partner in the Cwmfelin Tinplate Company. He was probably also connected with its successor, the Cwmfelin Works and Colliery Company (1880–1883). These two companies owned the Cwmfelin works before the Cwmfelin Tinplate Co. of 1883 which was created by Edward Rice Daniel and his brother-in-law John Jones Jenkins. Cefngyfelach, originally known as Pwll Bach, was situated a little to the north of Mynyddbach Chapel and west of Llangyfelach Road. It was the older and smaller of the two collieries (Cefngyfelach and Tirdonkin) and was sunk about 1887, initially as a private venture by Edward Rice Daniel (1829–1905), a leading figure in the tinplate industry to supply the Cwmfelin Tinplate Company and its successor the Cwmfelin Works and Colliery Company (1880–1883) with high quality bituminous coal.[3]

(Plate 6) Cwmfelin Tinplate Company Registration Stamp 1894

Pwll Bach was owned by the Cwmfelin Tinplate Co. (1893), to supply their tinworks with fuel. The shaft was 64 yards deep and ventilation was by means of a furnace.

From the Inspector of Mines list 1896, Cefn Gyfelach Colliery Co. Swansea, were the owners and they employed 116 men underground and 32 on the surface, producing House and Manufacturing coal; the manager at this time was William Morgan. In 1903 the company became the Tirdonkin Colliery Co., Ltd., who in 1908 employed 297 men underground and 59 on the surface with William H. Jones as the manager.[4]

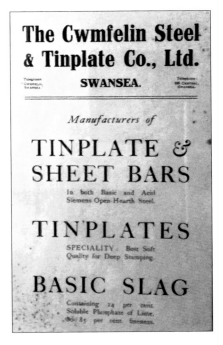

(Plate 7) Advertisement for Cwmfelin Products. Courtesy Brains Brewery 'Three Sisters Public House. (c) J.P.Thomas

The advertisement states the works were using the Siemens Open Hearth method of steel production. (This process was developed by William Siemens at the former Landore spelter works: See Chapter XIII Plate 19) The open hearth process is a batch process and a batch is called a "heat". The furnace is first inspected for possible damage. Once it is ready or repaired, it is charged with light scrap, such as sheet metal, shredded vehicles or waste metal. The furnace is heated using burning gas. Once it has melted, heavy scrap, such as building, construction or steel milling scrap is added, together with pig iron from blast furnaces. Once all the steel has melted, slag forming agents, such as limestone, are added. The oxygen in iron oxide and other impurities decarburize the pig iron by burning excess carbon away, forming steel. To increase the oxygen contents of the heat, iron ore can be added to the heat.

The furnace is tapped the same way a blast furnace is tapped; a hole is bored on the side of the hearth and the raw steel flows out. Once all the steel has been tapped, the slag is skimmed away. The raw steel can be cast into ingots; this process is called *teeming*.

(Plate 8) View of Cwmfelin Work's 'Three Sisters' open hearth furnace stacks from Carmarthen Road. Courtesy Brains Brewery 'Three Sisters' Public House. (c) J.P.Thomas

(Plate 9) Casting Pit at Cwmfelin Steel Works.
Courtesy Swansea Museum Collection.

(Plate 10) Workmen loading teemed cast steel ingots into railway
trucks at Cwmfelin works. The empty 'teeming' moulds can be seen
stored precariously nearby. Courtesy Swansea Museum Collection.

The works had enjoyed a reasonably good safety record, but in 1927 the local newpaper reported:

"Bursting of a Flywheel. THREE MEN INJURED AND PLANT DAMAGED. Swansea, Saturday. Through the sudden bursting a fly wheel at Cwmfelin Tinplate Works, Swansea, this morning, three men received injuries, though only one – Robert Edwards – was seriously hurt. Much damage was done to the running plant. Edwards was conveyed to hospital and detained, and there were many narrow escapes by others of the workmen."[5]

(Plate 11) View of Cwmfelin Works's 'Three Sisters' open hearth furnace stacks from Marsden Street, Greenhill. Courtesy West Glamorgan Archives.

(Plate 12) 1906 View of Cefngyfelach Colliery. At the time, Tirdonkin Colliery had already opened and the sidings were being used to store private coal trucks marked 'TIRDONKIN' SS 647979. Courtesy Treboeth History and Pictorial Record.

The Cefngyfelach colliery had no railway connection and coal had to be transported by horse and cart across Mynyddbach Common to a coal yard and screen at the north side of the junction of Llangyfelach Road and Cadle Road (then known as Heol Ddu). This was a slow, costly, and inefficient system, so in 1896 a mineral railway from Cefngyfelach was laid to the Great Western Railway at Cwmfelin. The contractor waas a G. Hanney, of Morriston, and the work was supervised by the colliery manager, William Morgan. The total cost was £7,000. Despite some difficulty in obtaining the land required, which lead to an alteration of the plans, work went ahead and within four months the two mile long railroad was ready to receive traffic. From the outset it was worked by steam locomotives, and the first one ran all the way up to Cefngyfelach on 1 May 1896. The following day the first trucks of coal were brought down and the new line was in business. The junction with the Great Western Railway at Cwmfelin faced east, making it easy for traffic to to be taken on to Swansea Docks or to be transferred to the Cwmfelin internal rail system.[6]

*(Plate 13) O.S. 1888 – 1913 Site Map of Cefngyfelach Colliery
following the opening of the railway. Note the unusual circular railway
track arrangement which made shunting operations easier.
Courtesy O.H.M.S.*

The first half mile or more of the railway climbed fairly steeply through Manselton, but it them levelled out and followed
the contours on the side of Mynydd Cadle through Penvilia,
Treboeth and Tirdeunaw. Below Penlan Fawr it crossed the
Vivians' Mynydd Newydd inclined railroad by a bridge. He engine shed was at Cwmfelin works, and an early setback occurred
soon after the line opened, when the shed caught fire and the
brand-new locomotive inside was damaged.[7]

274

(Plate 14) View of abandoned Cefngyfelach Colliery single track railway extension bridge parapets which supported a bridge crossing Penplas Road. SS 644984. 18 September 2018. (c) J.P. Thomas.

(Plate 15) Remains of abandoned Tirdonkin Colliery single track railway extension embankment at Bryntwood, Llangyfelach. SS 638986. The A48 trunk Road can be seen in the backgound. 24 January 2018. (c) J.P. Thomas.

275

In 1903 the company became the Tirdonkin Colliery Co., Ltd., who in 1908 employed 297 men underground and 59 on the surface with William H. Jones as the manager. The colliery worked the Three, Five and Six foot seams and was later linked underground to Tirdonkin colliery when it opened. The Three Foot seam in Cefyngyfelach was still being worked in 1908 when the Cambrian reported an accident there on 24 October 1908. The Six Foot seam must also have been reached by then, since it lies between the Five (Penvilian) and Three Foot seams. The method of working was by pillar and stall, the normal method of the day.[8]

The flow of air through the workings was encouraged by a furnace at the bottom of Pen-y-Pant ventilating shaft at Llangyfelach, which also helped the airflow in Pentre Pit. Possibly the ventilation arrangements were changed and the furnace extinguished at some date before Cefngyfelach ceased to work. There was also an air vent shaft known as Pwll Aer on Mynydd Cadle Common on a contour level with Cefngyfelach. This was an upcast shaft and served Cefngyfelach, Pentre, Cwm and probably Mynydd Newydd pits.[9]

In November 1908 Cefyngyfelach was closed and production concentrated on Tirdonkin, whose lease was increased from 600 to 1,050 acres in 1909. Sadly, the South Wales Daily Post reported on 30 June 1910 that at Cefyngyfelach, Llangyfelach, James Morgan, aged 29, was killed at the mine.

Even after Cefyngyfelach was abandoned as a productive colliery, it was retained as a ventilation shaft and as an emergency exit from the network of interconnecting workings in the area.[10]

Following the opening of the railway as far as Cefngyfelach, the way was now clear for Jenkins and Daniel to start on opening up new areas of coal. It had been intended all along that the Cefyngyfelch line should be the first stage, a springboard for further expansion, and that it should be extended north towards Llangyfelach village to serve the new pits to be developed in this area. The Cefn Gyfelach Colliery Company (CGCC) lost no time in doing this, for in June 1896 the expected expansion started when they began to sink a new shaft in a field near Cilfwnwr Farm between Llangyfelach and Penllegaer. Something was obviously wrong with their plans, however, for the sinking was abandoned without the pit coming into production.[11]

However, on 7th December, 1901, a ceremony was held to mark the beginning of sinking the new colliery in the woods of behind Tirdwncyn Farm. There were to be two shafts, an upcast and a downcast, and the first sods were cut by Captain Charles Llewelyn, the son of Sir John Llewelyn, and by Sir John's youngest daughter, Gladys. The two pits were names Charles Pit and Gladys Pit in their honour. They were to be 15 feet in diameter and to go down to a depth about 300 or 350 yards.[12]

The coal that was to be worked from the colliery was about the only substantial reserve left in the Swansea area and slotted between Vivian's Mynydd Newydd taking and Glasbrooks' Garngoch. It was estimated that there were 20 million tons waiting to be extracted. Jenkins had taken an initial lease of 600 acres from Sir John Dillwyn-Llewelyn, which was later to be extended to 1050 acres in 1909 and again to 1450 in 1912. The annual rent was to be £3,000, with an additional loyalty of 8d. per tonne on coal and 3d. per tonne on fireclay. The choice of the colliery site seems to have been imposed on him by Dillwyn-Llewelyn, who wanted the pit to be in the Tirdwncyn basin so that the pithead gear was not visible from Penllegaer House.[13]

Over the next few years steady, if not spectacular, progress was made. Work was concentrated on the Gladys pit at first, and on 6 September 1903 the five foot (Penvilian) seam was struck some 450 feet below the surface. At about this time a pair of horizontal winding engines were ordered from the Kilmarnock engineering firm of Andrew Barclay.[14]

The Five Foot seam was struck in the Charles pit in June 1904, and Tirdonkin became a fully working colliery in 1905. Working was by pillar and stall, filling six to eight tonnes a place. The trams were 5 feet long by 3 feet and six inches wide and had steel bodies and wooden frames with a capacity of between 21–25 hundred weight. The gauge was 2-feet and the rails used were 30 pounds T-headed in the headings and 22 pound bridge rails in the stalls.[15]

The next few years were a succesful period for TCC, but they were also years of heavy financial demands. As has been seen sinking continued to the Six Foot seam in both shafts. The striking of this seam in the Gladys Pit in 1908 meant that both seams were in production and the original intention of the company had been realised, but to achieve this it had been necessary to borrow heavily. Jenkins continued to lend money from his own estate, and large sums were borrowed from the Capital and Counties Bank under his guarantee. At this stage, money was being invested in the colliery all the time, but it was not yet sufficiently productive to return any sort of profit.

(Plate 16) 1900s view of Tirdonkin Coilliery. Courtesy Treboeth History and Pictorial Record. Note the privately owned 'TIRDONKIN' coal trucks in the railway siding.

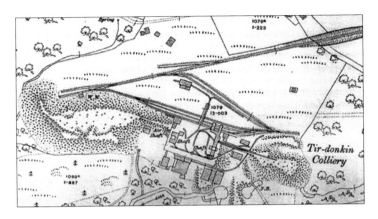

*(Plate 17) O.S. 1916 Site Map of Tirdonkin Colliery.
Courtesy O.H.M.S.*

However, the coal screening plant to the north of the colliery appears to have been a rather primitive contraption. The coal was tipped over a series of bars 24 feet long and 1 foot apart. The surface arrangements in general were not well designed. If they had been better laid out, the original expenditure would have been less and the surface working costs lower.[16] A report at the time described the surface layout in rather scathing terms:

"In my opinion the Surface Arrangements are by no means well designed and better advantage could have been taken of what was quite a good surface site for a pair of Pits. The layout of the Sidings is particularly objectionable necessitating two "back shunts" before the empty trucks are under the screens, and one "back shunt" for the full truck afterwards. If the Colliery had been laid out properly the original expenditure would have been less and the surface working costs lower."[17]

During August 1906 it was reported that in the previous year there had been a loss of £3,428, but the colliery was now beginning to pay. The striking of the Six Foot seam in the Gladys pit in 1908 meant that both seams were in production. The next few years were a period of expansion for the Tirdonkin Coal Company, but there were also years of heavy financial demands as sinking continued to the Three Foot seam in both shafts.[18]

In the latter part of 1903, the name of the company had been changed from the Cefngyfelach Colliery Company to Tirdonkin Collieries Company (TCC) to reflect the the shift in in the relative importance of the two collieries now that Tirdonkin was beginning to yield.[19]

In 1908 the Great Western Railway commenced its construction of the Swansea District avoiding line to serve as a bypass for the Fishguard to London (Paddington) boat trains and as a less congested route for coal traffic to the docks. The line was opened in sections between 1912 and 1915.[20]

The Tirdonkin Company put in a connection from this line to their colliery in about 1913, and the entire track of the original railway south from Cefngyfelach to Cwmfelin was closed and lifted. This was a definite improvement because the gradient on the incline from Tirdonkin to Cefyngyfelach was against the load and too steep for a locomotive to raise a loaded train up it. A stationary engine at Cefngyfelach had to be used and the two changes of motor power created additional expense.[21] On the other hand, under the new arrangements, trains from Tirdonkin had to reverse near the corner of Clawdd-y-duon Wood to get onto the new line, but this was a comparitively minor inconvenience for a line of this kind.[22]

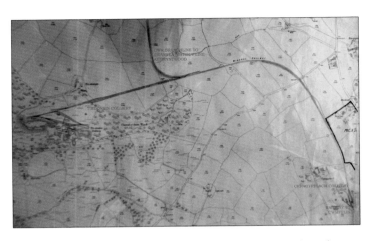

(Plate 18) O.S. 1917 Glamorganshire Map showing the railway extension from Cefngyfelach Colliery (bottom right) to Tirdonkin Colliery (middle left) and to the Great Western Railway at Bryntwood, Llangyfelach. Courtesy West Glamorgan Archives.

By 1910, output was down to 400 tonnes a day, an annual rate of 120,000 tonnes, owing to the ococcurance of an extensive fault (Tirdonkin) at Llangyfelach which had led to the abandonment of the Five Foot (Penvilian) seam the previous year. It seems to have remained at about this level until the Tirdonkin Merthyr Company took over.

The Tirdonkin lease was extended to 1,450 acres in 1912 when a new 60-year lease was taken out. In 1913 Tirdonkin colliery was managed by D. Howell and employed 234 men underground and 56 surface workers.[23]

However, the number of workers employed at the colliery fluctuated year by year. The mine was listed in 1913, 1917 and 1921 as being owned by the Tirdonkin Collieries Limited of Swansea. It employed 393 men in 1907, and 337 men in 1913–15 working the Swansea Five Foot seam at a section of 54 inches and producing steam and manufacturing coals with D. Howell as the manager. By 1916 there were 337 men employed with

Mr D. Howell still the manager. By 1923 it was owned by the Tirdonkin Merthyr Company and employed 588 men working underground and 172 men working at the surface, producing steam coal from the Three and Six Foot seams. In 1927 it employed 760 men with the manager being F. Hargreaves in both years. It abandoned the Three Foot seam in June 1928, when the closure of Calland's Pit [Landore] left it vulnerable to flooding.[24]

This was south Wales coal industry's period of greatest prosperity. By 1913 the area was the leading British coalfield in terms of export. The tinplate industry had also emerged from the depression of the 1890s and found new overseas markets.[25]

1917 Tirdonkin is reported to have supplied 42,073 tonnes to local works and 54,020 tonnes for shipment to France. The ports used were Swansea, Burry Port, Llanelli, Briton Ferry and Port Talbot. It was their dependence on the French market that created problems after the First World War, when demand from France was withdrawn.[26]

In 1915 Lord Glantawe, Chairman and managing Director of the TCC, died, and it was revealed that his estate was owed £175,364 by the Colliery Company. Moreover, it was shown that, in the previous five years, £28,000 had been spent on the colliery, mainly to comply with the terms of the lease, and two new drifts had been commenced, which were expected to cost £15,000, to win back the Five Foot (Penvilian) seam to the north west of the Tirdonkin fault and bring it back into production. Daniell considered satisfying the claims of Glantawe's estate by means of a cash payment combined with the issue of £100,000 debentures by the Colliery Company, but eventually decided to sell the colliery. The buyer, Lewis, Stephens and Co. of Swansea, purchased the colliery for £230,000. The old Tirdonkin Collieries was put into liquidation soon after and a new company was formed – The Tirdonkin Collieries Limited. Daniell acted as liquidator for the old company and he was fortunate to sell it at just the right time, judging by a letter written to him in December 1920 by W. Nicholas, Secretary of the TCC and a Swansea coal factor:

"Business is as nearly as bad as it can be just now as there are no buy-ers of Stem or Anthracite, Patent Fuel is also "sick". Large coal (the little that's wanted) is easily bought for 60/- & less & Thro' for less than 40/- shipment. But there is no demand, and until France returns for Welsh coal or new markets are found, things will be bad. Shipping companies must be badly hit. Whatever the future has in store, it is very clear that you sold the colliery at the right moment, and, I believe, not a day too soon."[27]

During 1918 work started on two new drifts to open out the Five Foot (Penvilian) seam again to the northwest of the Tirdonkin Fault, but it did not go very far, because in 1928 only the Six Foot seam was working. Like the Five Foot seam, this was very disturbed, which meant that the output of coal rarely came up to expectations. By this date the colliery was managed by William H. Jones and employed 362 men.

Then the export trade contracted after the first World War. Tirdonkin fell on hard times. H.C.M. Daniell, the son-in-law of John Jones Jenkins, who had controlled the company since the death of his father-in-law in 1915, sold it to a new compa-ny, Tirdonkin Merthyr Collieries Ltd. Under the new owners manning levels increased to nearly 600 underground and near-ly 200 on the surface, in an attempt to push up output to the 300,000 tonnes a year which was regarded as a profitable yield.[28]

Under its new management, Tirdonkin entered the most productive period of its existence. In March 1922, a record dai-ly output of 1,209 tonnes was achieved and the following July a weekly record of 7,419 tonnes, both well over the 300,000 tonnes per annum required to produce a reasonable profit. This new confidence caused to company to place an advertisement in newspapers and mining journals:

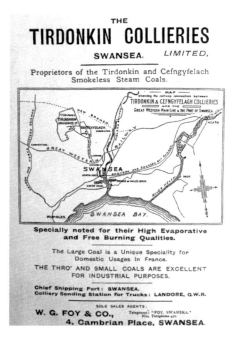

THE

TIRDONKIN COLLIERIES

SWANSEA. *LIMITED,*

Proprietors of the Tirdonkin and Cefngyfelach
Smokeless Steam Coals.

**Specially noted for their High Evaporative
and Free Burning Qualities.**

The Large Coal is a Unique Speciality for
Domestic Usages in France.

THE THRO' AND SMALL COALS ARE EXCELLENT
FOR INDUSTRIAL PURPOSES.

Chief Shipping Port: SWANSEA.
Colliery Sending Station for Trucks: LANDORE, G.W.R.

SOLE SALES AGENTS:

W. G. FOY & CO., Telegrams: "FOY, SWANSEA."
Nat. Telephone 472.
4, Cambrian Place, SWANSEA.

*(Plate 19) Advertisement for Tirdonkin Collieries, Swansea Limited,
for Smokeless Steam Coal. C.1912. Note the sending station for
coal trucks was LANDORE, GWR. Courtesy P. Reynolds.*

This period of prosperity was short-lived. All pits to the north-
west of Swansea were drained by a pumping engine at Calland's
Pit, Landore. In 1926 pumping ceased on the grounds of cost,
and the water level began to rise in all the neighbouring collieries. Eventually there was a great pond of water in the basin
between Landore, Morriston and Penllegaer, which extended
through the workings of several connected collieries.[29]

Although Tirdonkin workings did not actually form part of
the interconnecting workings of Calland's, Mynydd Newydd,
Pentre, Cefngyfelach and Copper Pit, the colliery had foolish-
ly penetrated the statutory 50 yard barrier of coal that should
have been left between Tirdonkin and Mynydd Newydd, and

284

so the water was able to percolate through the barrier and strata. Expensive new pumping equipment was installed in the Six Foot seam at Tirdonkin, the only seam being worked at the time, in an attempt to keep the water down, but this meant that it became uneconomic to work the coal. The water flooded in such a quantity as to drown out the pumps.[30]

Indeed, sinking to the Six Foot seam in both shafts had caused the company to borrow money and share certificates were issued in an attempt to raise capital of £70,000.

(Plate 20) Tirdonkin Collieries Share Certificate dated 4 August 1906. CourtesyTirdonkin Collieries Ltd. Amgueddfa. Cymru

In April 1928, it was decided to abandon the Six Foot seam and remove the machinery. About 600 men were made redundant, but this was considered to be a temporary measure as it was planned to put the Five Foot (Penvilian) seam back into production. It was hoped that, being on a higher level, it would be easier to keep dry. This would have taken about 12 or 15 months, but the financial arrangements broke down. A Receiver was called in and the Tirdonkin Merthyr Co. was put into liquidation.[31]

Given an annual rent of £3,000 and an additional royalty of 8d per tonne, an output of 1,000 tonnes per day was expected, working both the Five Foot and Six Foot seams. However, this ambitious target was never achieved, although the mine was at its most profitable in the early 1920s, with about 650 men then working underground and a further 170 on the surface. As the accompanying plan shows workings extended under most of Valley Woods, except for the site of the estate farms and the mansion itself. However, water from other collieries then began to rise, flooding Tirdonkin's workings.

Work ceased on April 28, 1928. Tirdonkin Colliery closed for good and the connection to the Great Western Railway Swansea District Line was also closed and lifted.[32]

The following map shows the extensive mine workings beneath the Penllegaer estate:

(Plate 21) Map of Tirdonkin Merthyr Collieries' plan of mine work-ings under the Penllegaer estate. The current A48 road can be seen at the bottom left of the map. Note that Tredegar-Fawr and Tir-Fford farm buldings and also Penllegaer House, situated to the southwest, do not stand over mine workings, presumably to avoid the possibili-ty of subsidence. The probable position of the 'Tirdonkin Fault' which halted John Morris' Clyndu Level Colliery's Five Foot (Penvilian) mining activities at Llangyfelach is also shown. The map was drawn on linen paper which shows signs of deteroration. SS 632997. Courtesy West Glamorgan Archives. GB 216 D/D PT 29.

Little is known about the day-to-day working of the railway line. A part from the incline north of Cefyngyfelach, was worked throughout by locomotives and it is known that in 1918 the Tirdonkin Colliery Company had one locomotive, an 0-6-0 tank engine built by the Yorkshire Engine Company of Sheffield, which had been acquired in 1915, For a short period in 1916 they were also owners of 0-6-0 locomotive 'SWANSEA'.[33]

The locomotive 'SWANSEA' had a chequered history: It was acquired in about 1913 by Powland and Mason, the GWR carting agents in Swansea and hauling agents for GWR traffic on the Swansea Harbour Trust lines. Powland and Mason sold the locomotive to the Cwmfelin Steel and Tinplate Works (owners of the steeply graded Cwmfelin and Cefngyfelach colliery line, Swansea). Towards the end of 1918, it was sold to the Bynea Steel Works, Llanelli, where it remained until withdrawn for preservation in 1962 at Middleton, Leeds.

(Plate 22) Avonside 0-6-0 saddle tank steam locomotive No.1569 'SWANSEA' stands forlorn in a siding at the Middleton Railway Preservation Society's yard in 1962, before being sold to a private collector who, unfortunately, had it scrapped. Courtesy Andrew Gill, Middleton Railway Preservation Society.

These days little evidence remains of Cefngyfelach colliery, and at Tirdonkin the shafts were filled in and capped by the Forestry Commission in 1969–70, and the land reclaimed. The former mineral railway can be followed for most of its length north of Cefngyfelach, but south to Cwmfelin, little, if any, remains. Both collieries failed to come up to the expectations of their promoters and lasted only comparitively short periods, but in their day they played their part in the local economy, as suppliers of coal to the steel smelting industry and places of employment.[34]

In the next and last chapter we will be looking at the claims made by writers that John Morris and Thomas Lockwood's Clyndu Level Colliery, Morriston, had incorporated an underground navigational canal into its coal transportation system, 'this being the earliest example of canals being used for underground mine transport in the world.'

CHAPTER XV
BIBLIOGRAPHY AND ILLUSTRATIONS

(1) The Penllegaer Trust Archive Fact Sheet (un–dated)
(2) Treboeth Historical & Pictorial Record.Treboeth Historical Society, 2012, p.99.
(3) Ibid p.99.
(4) Welsh Coal Mines Forum, un–numbered page.
(5) Grace's Guide to British Industrial History, 1927.
(6) 'Two Swansea Collieries: Cefngyfelach and Tirdonkin, Paul Reynolds, Welsh Journals Online,Vol. 32, 1 Jan. 1981. p.62.
(7) Ibid.
(8) Treboeth Historical & Pictorial Record, p.100.
(9) Ibid. p.101.
(10) Ibid.
(11) 'Two Swansea Collieries', Paul Reynolds, p.62.
(12) Ibid, p.63.

(13) Ibid.

(14) Ibid.

(15) 'Treboeth Historical & Pictorial Record', p.101.

(16) Ibid.

(17) Two Swansea Collieries, Paul Reynolds', p.68

(18) Ibid, p.101.

(19) Ibid, p.65.

(20) 'Treboeth Historical & Pictorial Record', p.101

(21) Ibid.102

(22) 'Two Swansea Collieries', Paul Reynolds, p.62

(23) Ibid.

(24) Welsh Coal Mines (un–numbered page)

(25) 'Treboeth Historical & Pictorial Record',

(26) Ibid. p.10

(27) Two Swansea Collieries, Paul Reynolds, p.66.

(28) 'Treboeth Historical & Pictorial Record. p.103.

(29) Ibid.

(30) Ibid.

(31) Ibid.

(32) Ibid.

(33) 'Two Swansea Collieries, Paul Reynolds, p.70.

(34) Ibid

(Plate 1) 1904 View of Penllegaer House.

(Plate 2) 1946 RAF Aerial View of Cwmfelin Steel and Tinplate Works, Cwmbwrla.

(Plate 3) 1916 O.S. Site Map of Cwmfelin Steel and Tinplate Works, Cwmbwrla.

(Plate 4) 1800's Street Scene in Llangyfelach Road adjacent to Works.

(Plate 5) 1980's View of Cwmfelin Works at junction of Ysgubor Fach Street and Llangyfelach Road.

(Plate 6) Cwmfelin Tinplate Company Registration Stamp 1894

(Plate 7) Advertisement for Cwmfelin Works Products.

(Plate 8) View of Cwmfelin Work's 'Three Sisters' furnace stacks from Carmarthen Road.

(Plate 9) Casting Pit at Cwmfelin Steel Works.

(Plate 10) Workmen loading cast steel ingots into railway trucks at Cwmfelin Works.

(Plate 11) View of Cwmfelin Work's 'Three Sisters' furnace stacks from Marsden Street, Greenhill.

(Plate 12) 1906 View of Cefngyfelach Colliery.

(Plate 13) 1888–1913 O.S. Site Map of Cefngyfelach Colliery.

(Plate 14) Abandoned Cefngyfelach Colliery railway extension bridge abutment. 18 September 2018

(Plate 15) Remains of abandoned Tirdonkin Colliery single track railway extension embankment at Bryntwood, Llangyfelach. SS 638986. The A48 trunk Road can be seen in the backgound. 24 January 2019. J.P. Thomas

(Plate 16) 1900's View of Tirdonkin Colliery.

(Plate 17) 1916 O.S. Site Map of Tirdonkin Colliery.

(Plate 18) 1917 O.S. Map showing railway extension from Cefngyfelach Colliery to Tirdonkin Colliery and to the Great Western Railway at Bryntwood.

(Plate 19) 1912 Advertisement for Tirdonkin Collieries Smokeless Steam Coal.

(Plate 20) Tirdonkin Collieries Share Certificate dated 4 August 1906.

(Plate 21) Map of Tirdonkin Merthyr Collieries, Plan of Four Foot workings under the Penllegaer Estate.

(Plate 22) Avonside 0-6-0 saddle tank steam locomotive No.1569 'SWANSEA' stands forlorn in a siding at the Middleton Railway Preservation Society's yard in 1962.

CHAPTER XVI

THE MYTH OF THE CLYNDU UNDERGROUND NAVIGATIONAL CANAL

"The earliest known colliery in the Swansea district worked by means of a canal and wooden barges was the Brynlloi Pit in Cwmamman which dates as far back as 1757. It was managed on a very small scale, with local people obtaining the coal for domestic use. Its length was 640 links, about 5 feet 6 inches of headroom, and the sides cut upright like walls: the width of the canal was put at 4 feet 4 inches. At the far end of the canal there was an incline 145 links long, rising at a grade of about 1 foot per yard until it reached the coal bed. In the old workings, on the incline, there was the old 'hurdle' that was used on top of the boat. There were also the remains of old posts and one pair of timbers mortised to fit like the frame of a door. It appears that the coal was allowed to descend over the incline in a 'dray', or small cart, by a rope or light chain from a winder which was at the top. The coal was worked by the old method of pillar and stall, with a bank on one side."

(From an essay written by D. Trumor Thomas in 1894, titled "Hên Gymeriadau Plwyf y Betws")[1]

However, our review of the Graig Trewyddfa collieries serving the Morriston copperworks has not uncovered any such evidence to suggest a navigational canal was incorporated into the Clyndu Level Colliery workings, and many of the claims of the canal's existence appear to be pure speculation and hearsay. So we will look again at the writers' accounts over the last 200 years and determine whether the navigational canal's existence was a reality or a myth.

We will begin with an account recently given by the Morriston Historical Group:[2]

"The Clyndu underground canal was probably built by Lockwood, Morris and Co. It was constructed during the 1770s beneath Graig Trewyddfa at Morriston and has claims to have been the world's longest underground canal of its type. It was the first navigational canal ever built. Coal was brought from the coal-face in two ton wagons, which were then tipped into boats on the underground canal, each boat held two wagons or four tons of coal. The boats were three feet wide and twenty feet long. The boats were floated along the underground canal to a basin, then into Swansea Canal which ran from the Forest Copper-works in the north to Landore Copper-works at the south end."

However, the account is bare of any factual evidence of the underground canal's actual location. The reference to the dimensions of the canal boats and their loads of coal has been taken from a handwritten statement allegedly made by a 75-year old man in 1846, who had worked for Lockwood, Morris & Co.[3]

One of the earliest observers to assert the existence of the Clyndu underground canal was the Swedish observer, Eric Swadenstierna, who was shown around the Swansea industrial area by John Morris II in 1802-3 and was given all the necessary information by him and a Mr.Lockwood who owned coalmines and copperworks. He also had unrestricted admission to the latter's works, and permission to inquire about the methods of working.

Swedenstriera reported the following:

"… the Swansea Canal … boats one of which often only carries 2 to 3 tons [a loading of three and not four tons would have given the correct total loading of 1 Wey' as given in the earlier description]either go over branch canals constructed for the purpose, directly to some landing place [an allusion to the Trewyddfa Canal Incline?] or the coal is again transferred into the above described wagons. Occasionally also these little boats go a whole English mile or more underground, and take on their loads in the mine itself.

[Other small canals] are conducted to some copper works or to the places on the River Tavey [Tawe] where there are larger or smaller collecting places, where several boats at once can be unloaded comfortably. At one of the copper works such a collecting place or basin was laid out at the same level as the eaves of the roof of the building, so that the boates, which went to the coal mine a Swedish mile underground on one of the small canals, could on their return empty their loads directly into the smelting house." [4]

However, a perusal of Svedenstierna's account of his travels in the lower Swansea valley shows no evidence to say he actually visited the Clyndu Level colliery, but he clearly describes his visit to the Pentre colliery and the engine house at Glandwr (Landore). [5]

The copperworks to which he is referring is probably the Landore copper works, and Chapter 1, Plate 2, shows a water leat, not a canal, crossing a stone aquaduct, entering the works at roof level, powering an overshot water in the manufacturing house.

However, S. Hughes commented:

"He [Swedenstierna] is known not to be an absolutely reliable source, and hurried observation of the underground Clyndu Canal and the adjoining aquaduct which passes over the Trewyddfa Canal and supplied water to the Forest CopperWorks are probably the basis of his comments." [6]

*(Plate 1) We can see from a 1959 photograph of the surviving aqua-
duct at Copper Pit railway halt, in 1959, that it comprised a cast iron
trough fed by a watercourse, supported by stone parapets which crossed
the Swansea Canal (which included the Trewydda Canal section) to
the Forest Copperworks. The aquaduct had no capacity for coal boats
and where it met the steep ridge embankment, unsuitable to support
a surface tramway, there was little space or headroom to accommodate
a tunnel or level, so Swedenstierna's account is doubtful. Moreover
an 1882 coloured drawing of the Copper Pit area of lower Morriston
shows the steep ridge leading down to the canal from the Swansea
Turnpike Road but there is no evidence of the remains of a navigational canal nor a tunnel entrance. (See Plate 6)*

(Plate 2) A 1959 view taken in the opposite direction looking south towards Plasmarl showing a similar terrain with a steep ridge embankment unsuitable to support a surface tramway incline. The white building in the top right hand of the picture is the 'Duke' public house, which survives to this day. Courtesy Stations UK.

Many writers claiming the existence of the Clyndu Level underground mining canal have relied on a hand written statement allegedly made by a 75-year old man in 1846, who had worked for Lockwood. Morris & Co. before the passing of the Canal Act (Swansea).

4 Tons — that is 3 Boats were
called 1 Way.

The Boats were 3 feet wide + 20
feet long.

When the Boats first came out from
the level they entered a sort of Basin
& thus got into Lockwoods Canal which
ran from the Forrest Copper Works at
North end, to opposite the old Forge
just beyond the Landore Copper Works
at its South end.

That Canal was 4 feet wide at
the bottom & 8 feet wide at Top
with 4½ feet deep.

It occupied the lower side of the present
Canal

after the passing of the Act the Duke &
Messrs Lockwood lengthened — Widened.

(Plate 3) Clyndu Canal Transcript (Part) COP01/27 Copperopolis,
Landscapes of the Early Industrial Period in Swansea.
Stephen Hughes. 2000 p.100.

The full transcript reads as follows:

"the [Lockwood Morris & Co] canal was a continuation of the Underground Level called the Clyndee Level…"

His description of the level continued:

"The Clyndee Level … extended abt 1100 yards under the Mountain to the face of the Coal in the 5 feet or Penyvillia Vein. That level was 4ft 7? Inches wide and 8 feet high arched with Stone part of the way in – it still exists as a Waterway from the Coal Works as perfect as ever so far as it is arched, but further in it is [sic] Crept together in places so as not be of the full size.

Boats went up that level to the face of the Coal where the Waggons were tipped into them – each boat held 2 Waggons full – or 4 tons- that is 3 Boats were called 1 Wey The Boats were 3 feet wide & 20 feet long

   When the Boats first came from the level they entered a sort of Basin & they got into Lockwood's Canal which ran from the Forest Copper Works at North end: to opposite the old Forge just beyond the Landore Copper Works, at its South end.

   That Canal [Trewydda] was 4 feet wide at the bottom & 8 feet wide at top & 4 feet deep.

   It occupied the lower side of the present Canal.

   After the passing of the Act [Swansea Canal], the Duke and Messr Lockwood lengthened – widened [the Canal]."

Source: Clyndu Canal Transcript RCAHMW Copperopolis Pub COP01/27. Copperopolis, Landscapes of the Early Industrial Period in Swansea, Stephen Hughes. 2000 p.100.
   Some confusion here. When Lockwood and Morris built a new copperworks down river at Landore, they immediately extended the Clyndu [Trewyddfa] Canal southwards past the Birmingham and Rose Copperworks to the new site, just short of today's Landore Viaduct. This mile long "coal tub boat" canal was called Lockwood's Canal by Rees Morgan (Witness)

or Morris's Canal. It was apparently built without permission of Parliament or anyone else, and in about 1794 it was incorporated into the Swansea Canal.

The Clyndu Level Colliery entrance was situated at Tycoch, Uplands Terrace, Morriston, about 178.9 feet[6] above the Tawe valley floor, and probably did extend some 1100 yards under Graig Trewyddfa. To claim the Lockwood Morris & Co. Trewyddfa Canal, situated on the valley floor, was a continuation of the 'underground level' called the Clyndu Level would clearly defy the laws of gravity.[7]

In 1925, 'The Cambrian Daily Leader', reported an article "Morriston 80 years ago" by Oakley Walters J.P.

"An older, though perhaps better known today, colliery was the Old Clyndu Level. This was worked by small trams, which were taken in and out the level by horse tramway... The mined coal was taken down by horse tramway past Pentremawled and over the Graig to the Canal, to be discharged into boats at a point adjacent to the site of the present Spelter Works. This level ceased working in 1841."

Walters is correctly referring to coal being transported from the Clyndu Level to the Swansea Canal near the Spelter works utilising the Pentremawled Waggonway, which joined the Clyndu Wagonway near Uplands Terrace.

Walters continues his account by stating:

"In 1727, the Llangefelach Copper Works was commenced on the site of Vivian & Sons present Spelter Works. The works included brass and copper wire mills and sheet mills, together with battery works engaged in turning out commodities for the Government... Every workman, prior to his employment had to swear to keep the secret of the copper smelting process. The laboratory for testing the copper ore before treatment was built in 1747... it stood on the left hand side before you enter the present bridge [old bridge] across the river to the Beaufort. I well remember this old building, only demolished in recent years, and its sundial placed prominently in front of the house. Coal was supplied from the old Clyndu Level by an underground canal. The opening of the old canal is to be seen at present on the railway near Copper Pit siding."(8)

Walters is correctly referring to coal being transported from the Clyndu Level to the Swansea Canal near the Spelter works utilisling the Pentremawled Wagonway which joined the Clyndu Wagonway near Uplands Terrace, following a straight line route to the canal and Forest copperworks.

There appears to be some confusion here. The Llangyfelach Copperworks was situated in Landore, not Morriston. The Beaufort Bridge (*old bridge*) crossed the river Tawe at a point where the Forest Copperworks was sited Chapter V!, Plate 2). The copperworks received its smelting coal from the Clyndu Level in Uplands Terrace, Morriston, using an inclined waggonway, now known as Clyndu Street. Moreover, the Copper Pit railway siding, where the opening of the *'old canal opening'* was situated, was constructed on the valley floor not far from the Forest works. However, we do not have a definitive historical date of these observations. Roberts is probably referring to the Clyndu Tramway tunnel portal on the valley floor, where horses would be seen hauling waggons of coal, originating at the Clyndu Level Colliery, to the Forest works.

P.R. Reynolds, in his 1976 South West Wales Industrial Archaeology Society Paper on the Clyndu Tramway, stated:

"It is not surprising since it owes it's origins to an earlier waggonway by which coal was brought down from levels on the side of the valley... A waggonway, now Clyndu Street, was built and it ran in a straight line from the mouth of the level to the copperworks.

The first definite reference we have to the waggonway is on a map drawn in 1761 from survey made a few years previously." [9]

Interestingly, Reynolds makes no reference to a 'Clyndu Boat Level'.

In 2008, a paper prepared A. Sherman (Leadfield, Swansea) claimed:

"An underground canal built by Robert Morris to transport coal directly from Swansea's 5ft coal seam to the processing site. It is generally thought that this canal was constructed in the 1770's, however some secondary sources suggest that it may have been built as early as 1747. If this early construction date is correct, it would make the Clyn-Du level the earliest example of canals being used for underground mine transport in the world."[10]

However, Sherman is referring to the Clyndu Level Colliery, which was known to have been in production in 1754 (when an accident occured), situated at Tycoch, near Uplands Terrace, Upper Morriston. To say the Clyn-Du-level is the earliest example of canals being used for underground mine transport in the world is pure speculation.

In 2008 R. Rees wrote in 'The Black Mystery' 2008 p.61:

"At his Clyndu colliery (c1754) just outside Morriston, Morris drove a level, eight feet high and nearly five wide, eleven hundred yards under the mountain. There was so much water that boats three feet wide and twenty long, with a capacity of two wagons or four tons, could, in a narrow channel, float up the heading to a point where the laden wagons could be tipped into them. It was, so it has been claimed, the first navigational or underground canal ever built. Boats emerged from the level into what has been described as a sort of basin and from it entered a canal that led to the Forest works. Coal not destined for the work served what had been a thriving export trade from Swansea."[11]

Surprisingly, Rees took the view that the Clyndu Colliery was the 'first navigational or underground canal ever built' and that boats emerged from the level into what has been described as a sort of basin and from there entered a canal that led to the Forest works. However, the Clyndu Level Colliery was situated at Tycoch, near Uplands Terrace, higher Morriston, while the Forest Copperworks was built on the valley floor. It would have been virtually impossible to link the two by means of a canal, even with an underground pound lock.

Interestingly, Paul Reynolds of the Morriston Library History Group wrote in 2015:

"There were two Clyndu levels, the upper 'dry' level and the lower boat level at the foot of the Graig near the present-day Duke's Arms. Both were opened in around 1750 by Lockwood, Morris & Co under their 1746 lease from the Duke of Beaufort. Their primary purpose was to supply coal to the Forest copperworks which was opened at the same time (1747/8). Clyndu 'dry' level was in existence by 1754 when a fatality is recorded in a Clyndu level. However, it is possible that this fatality occurred in Clyndu Boat Level which was probably in the process of being opened in 1753/4. Lewis Thomas' map of 1761 shows the level and a coal road running down to the copperworks which is explicitly labelled as 'The road where John Morris's carts bring down the Coal to the Copper works'. Clyndu Street follows the course of this road. The level worked the Five Foot vein. It remained the property of Lockwood, Morris & Co and continued to be worked even after the Forest works was closed in about 1790."[(12)]

Reynolds' claim that there were two Clyndu levels, the upper 'dry' level and the lower boat level at the foot of the Graig near the present day Duke's Arms; both opening in around 1750 by Lockwood, Morris & Co. is pure speculation with no firm supporting evidence; our research at the City and County of Swansea Planning Department shows that the lower boat level was in fact the Clyndu Level tramway tunnel. However, the underground canal to which he makes reference was undoubtedly the Graig Trewyddfa underground water drainage canal, which originated at Clase Bach, and fed the 'Water Machine Pit' sited close to the junction of Vicarage Road and Cwm Bath Road, providing power to a capstan shaft by means of a water-driven wheel.[(13)]

Moreover, his claim that a fatality which occurred in the Clyndu Level Colliery in 1754, (in fact, six colliers were suffocated by carbonic gas poisoning) *'possibly'* occurred in the Clyndu Boat Level, bears no supporting evidence (See Chapter II).

Peter Rickets, in 'Visit South Wales Canals', Neath and Tennant Canal Trust, stated:

"Located between Landore and Morriston, it extended approximately 1 mile into coal workings under Graig Trewyddfa. The date of the Clyndu Level is given as 1747 by George Grant in his second edition of 'Copper Smelting in Glamorganshire' published in 1881, while other sources give the date as later in the 1770s. It is reasonable to date the level as 1747–48 as this is the date that coincides with the building of the Forest Copper Works and the Clyndu Colliery. The coal extracted was used to fuel the the Forest Works: both the colliery and the works belonged to Lockwood Morris & Co. Boats using the underground canal were 3ft wide and 20 ft long carrying 3 tons."[14]

Rickets was clearly referring to the Clyndu Level Colliery at Tycoch, Uplands Terrace, not a Boat Level Colliery, and the earlier claim by a Swedish observer that boats using the canal were 3 feet wide and 20 feet long carrying 3 tonnes was deemed by him to be unreliable.

Moreover, a perusal of both the Badmington and Morris manuscripts collection of the period shows no mention of a 'Clyndu navigational or boat level canal'.

S. Hughes himself had expressed his doubts over the existence of the Clyndu navigational canal:

"However, there are reasons to question the construction of Clyndu Level (Canal) at a date prior to 1761. It does not show the mouth of the coal level in the works (copper) site, or the site, or any of the ventilation shafts to it, although it does show the pumping shaft (engine house) at Clyndu which went down to the tunnel."[15] What tunnel Hughes is referring to remains a mystery.

The account of Clyndu given by a John Bateman who visited the colliery in 1805 makes no mention of boats; he simply states that fillers are paid 2s/6d a wey for Filling at the faces and taking the Coals out to the day along a Level of 700 Yards Long, exclusive of horse work. No mention of a navigational canal.[16]

An important document which needs to be considered is Sir John Morris's 1854 lease of mining assets in the Fee of Trewyddfa to Phillip Richard and John Glasbrook, both of Swansea, colliery proprietors and copartners.[17] The schedule of mining assets for the collieries in the lease are as follows:

AT CLYNDU: Engine House and Pit.

AT COPPER PIT: One 14 inch high pressure Steam Engine complete except the brass fittings and sweep rods. Two Boilers and fittings complete. Pumping apparatus and a lift of 8 inches. Pumps complete. Pit Top complete.

AT GRAIG PIT: Pit and Horseway.

AT LANDORE PUMPING PIT: Two Boilers and fittings 30 feet long by 6 feet Diameter complete. An old cylinder fit for a casing for a smaller engine. Engine House. Great. A pump pit and rods and two old capstans.

AT LANDORE COAL PIT: 14 inch Condensing Engine and Boiler complete.

AT CWM PIT: Boiler and fittings 34 feet long by five feet diameter complete. 36 inch pumping Engine of low pressure complete except the nozels and gearing. 80 fathoms of pumps and rods complete. Great and capstan shaft complete.

The mining assets at Clyndu are listed as Engine House and Pit, but there is no mention of a Navigational Canal; yet the Graig's 'Pit and Horseway' is listed. A navigational canal for the transportation of mined coal would have been an important asset and its absence from the lease throws serious doubt on its existence.

Indeed, when Arthur Pendarves Vivian visited Cwm Level Colliery in 1868, he reported:[18]

"We went in the trams about I 1/2 miles – the 5ft.looks very well here and cuts nice and large and the measures look quiet and at an easy angle. We crossed over one fault, a 1 fathom upturn west. This ground is all full of old workings and there are no less than 5 levels driven in this neighbourhood in this vein of which one is Clyndu. They are in fact in this level only scraping out the leavings of the old people."

Yet, although Pengreaves was inspecting the 5 feet measures (Penvillian Vein and its remnants) at Clyndu, there was no report of finding a navigational canal among the workings.

However, Stephen Hughes went to great lengths to produce an artist's impression of where the navigational tunnel was supposedly located, but overlooked the straight-line construction of the Clyndu Tramroad from Uplands Terrace to its direct entrance into the Forest Copper Works. [19]

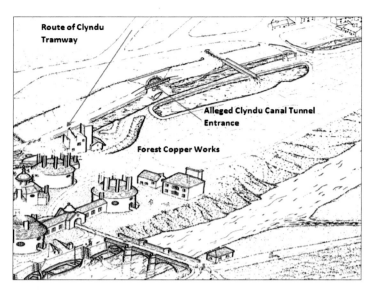

Route of Clyndu Tramway

Alleged Clyndu Canal Tunnel Entrance

Forest Copper Works

(Plate 4) Artist's Impression of where the Clyndu Level Navigational Canal Tunnel was thought to be located. The canal entrance was shown to be located close to the aquaduct at Copper Pit Railway Halt, Morriston. The author has added additional information in red showing the likely Clyndu Navigational Canal Tunnel Entrance and the route of the Clyndu Tramroad. SS 669972. Courtesy S.Hughes, Copperopolis Landscapes of The Early Industrial Period in Swansea, 2000, p.135.

The artist's impression produced by S. Hughes is an attempt to qualify the existence of a Clyndu ' navigational canal', the entrance being just south of the aquaduct at the Copper Pit Station site. However photographs taken at the same location in 1959 shows the aquaduct but no earthwork disturbance where a canal tunnel entrance may have been located. (See Chapter VII Plates 1 & 2) Clearly, the research by P.R. Reynolds on the route of the Clyndu Tramway has not been fully considered.[20]

However to say the pumping shaft of the Fire Engine Coalery engine house went down the 'navigational canal tunnel' bears no supporting evidence.

Moreover, an aerial view of the likely route of the Clyndu Tramway to the Forest works (Plate 4) shows evidence of new building work at the Copper Pit railway halt site, avoiding the line of the former tramway tunnel.

(Plate 5) Aerial view of the site of Clyndu Incline Tunnel Portal (Copper Pit Railway Siding) and Forest Copperworks. Interestingly none of the Toyota's surface buildings are built over the tunnel route, probably due to the possibility of subsidence. Courtesy Maps of Scotland SS 669972 November 2018.

Finally, in November 1908, the Swansea Waters and Sewers Committee met in April 1909 to discuss a proposal to construct an underground reservoir in the workings of the disused Clyndu Level Colliery. Having examined the coal workings of the Level, Mr. D.W.A. Saunders, a mining expert, reported his findings as to the suitability of this site, but there was no mention of finding the remains of a navigational canal for the transportation of coal.[21]

(Plate 6) 1882 Sketch of Lower Morriston near Copper Pit Colliery looking south before the construction of the GWR Morriston Branch Railway The steep ridge can be seen but there is no evidence of the remains of a navigational canal tunnel entrance as suggested by Stephen Hughes. The wooden fencing was still in situate in 1959 (See Plate 1). Courtesy Swansea University Library (Richard Burton Archives).

The writers' accounts provided so far, coupled with our review of the Trewyddfa collieries serving the Morriston copperworks have not uncovered any evidence to support the claim that a navigational canal was incorporated into the Clyndu Level Colliery workings. It would also appear that writers have tended to read ordnance survey maps without contours, resulting in their view of the topography of the Clyndu Level landscape becoming distorted. Moreover, the underground canal, to which writers makes reference, was undoubtedly the Graig Trewyddfa underground water drainage canal, which originated at Clase Bach, and fed the 'Water Machine Pit' sited close to the junction of Vicarage Road and Cwm Bath Road, providing power to a capstan shaft by means of a water-driven wheel. Indeed, with the absence of any tangible evidence to support writers' hunches that an underground navigational canal existed in the Clyndu Level mine, we are led to the conclusion that this means of coal transportation never existed in the level.

CHAPTER XVI
BIBLIOGRAPHY AND ILLUSTRATIONS

(1) From an essay written by D. Trumor Thomas in 1894, title 'Hên Gymeriadau Plwyf y Betws', quoted in 'Some Captured History of Glanamman', p.1.

(2) Morriston Historical and Pictorial Record. February, 2016.

(3) Clyndu Canal Transcript (Part) COP01/27Copperopolis, Landscapes of the Early Industrial Period in Swansea, Stephen Hughes, RCAHMW, 2000, p.100.

(4) Eric Svedenstierna, a Tourist, who was shown around the Swansea industrial area by John Morris II in 1802-3 and was given all the necessary information by him and a Mr.Lockwood who owned coalmines and copperworks... He also had unrestricted admission to the latter's works, and permission to inquire about the methods of working.

(5) Eric Svedenstierna, Svedenstierna's Tour of Great Britain 1802–3, The Travel Diary of an Industrial Spy. David & Charles,1973, pp. 38–49.

(6) S.Hughes, Copperopolis Landscapes of The Early Industrial Period in Swansea, RCAHMW, 2000, p.135

(7) Clyndu Canal Transcript (Part) COP01/27Copperopolis, Landscapes of the Early Industrial Period in Swansea Stephen Hughes, RCAHMW, 2000 p.100.

(8) 'The Cambrian Daily Leader', 31 July,1925, reported an article "Morriston 80 years ago" written by Oakley Walters J.P.

(9) P.R. Reynolds, 'South West Wales Industrial Archaeology Society Paper on the the Clyndu and Pentremawled Tramroads', 1976. (un–numbered page)

(10) A. Sherman, Leadfield Archaeology desk based assessment February 2008.

(11) 2008 R.Rees 'The Black Mystery', Y Lolfa, 2008 p.61

(12) P.R. Reynolds, 'South West Wales Industrial Archaeology Society Paper on the the Clyndu and Pentremawled Tramroads', 1976. (un–numbered page)

(13) See Chapter V (Water Machine Pit)

(14) Peter Rickets, 'Visit South Wales Canals' Neath and Tennant Canal Trust,

(15) S.Hughes, Copperopolis Landscapes of The Early Industrial Period in Swansea, RCAHMW, 2000, p.135

(16) Morriston Historical and Pictorial Record. February, 2016.

(17) Lease of Coal Mines in the Fee of Trewyddfa in The County of Glamorgan from Henry Charles Fitz Roy, Duke of Beaufort to Phillip Richard and John Glasbrook, both of Swansea, colliery proprietors and copartners dated 2 October 1854. West Glamorgan Archives Ref: D/D SB 15/16.

(18) 'The Vivian Collieries', F.G. Cowley, Welsh Journals on Line Vol.24, 1973, p.80.

(19) S. Hughes, Copperopolis Landscapes of The Early Industrial Period in Swansea, RCAHMW, 2000, p.135

(20) P.R. Reynolds, 'South West Wales Industrial Archaeology Society Paper on the the Clyndu and Pentremawled Tramroads', 1976. (un-numbered page)

(21) 'Cambrian', 27 November 1908, p.5.

(Plate 1) Photograph of the surviving aquaduct at Copper Pit railway halt, in 1959.

(Plate 2) Photograph of Copper Pit railway halt looking in direction of Plasmarl, 1959.

(Plate 3) Clyndu Canal Transcript (Part) COP01/27Copperopolis, Landscapes of the Early Industrial Period in Swansea, Stephen Hughes. 2000 p.100.

(Plate 4) Artists Impression of where the Clyndu Level Navigational Canal Tunnel was thought to be located. The canal entrance was shown to be located close to the aquaduct at Copper Pit Railway Halt, Morriston. Courtesy S.Hughes, Copperopolis Landscapes of The Early Industrial Period in Swansea. 2000, p.135

(Plate 5) Aerial view of the likely site of Clyndu Incline
Tunnel Portal (Copper Pit Railway Siding) and Forest
Copperworks.
(Plate 6) Sketch of Lower Morriston, near Copper Pit
Colliery looking south before the construction of the
GWR Morriston Branch Railway.

CHAPTER XVII

EPILOGUE

The purpose of this account is not to examine the pollution caused by the copper works in the lower Swansea Valley, which is well documented, but to focus attention on the demands placed by the hungry copper smelters on the coal owners and the local mining communities situated in the lower Swansea valley, who were employed in the bowels of the earth to cut out the coal to feed them. As there was no mechanised coal cutting machinery at this time, colliers and their families, including children, worked in dark, dismal, and dangerous conditions, while only using basic hand cutting tools. Miners worked in very confined spaces, as the coal seams in the Swansea district varied in thickness from eighteen inches to Five or Six Foot. Where possible, pit ponies were used to carry the coal. In narrow seams, however, women and children crawled on their hands and knees carrying the coal. Children could be chained, belted, or harnessed to a coal cart, more than half-naked, crawling with their heavy loads dragging behind them. Deformities were common among children who worked in the mines.

Moreover, pockets of methane gas were common, awaiting ignition by a spark from the clashing of steel tools or open candlelight. This was the terrible price paid by young miners who pushed or dragged the coal carts that turned the wheels that drove the industrial revolution and copperopolis.

The use of coal for copper smelting was certainly one justification for the concentration of copperworks in South Wales. Very large quantities of copper ores and regulus were brought to Swansea to be smelted from far and wide, because it cost less to bring the ore to the coal than to send the coal to the ore. The local gentry found the profits from the exploitation of the mineral resources of their estates a welcome addition to an agricultural income limited by the generally poor land of the area during this period of the development of mining and copper smelting in eighteenth century south Wales; land by which had hitherto been fit only for the grazing of sheep thus acquired a new importance and bitter disputes over the ownership of particular pieces of ground previously considered worthless were frequent.

While freeholders held the rights to the minerals under their own land, the Duke of Beaufort claimed the minerals under the commons and copyhold lands in the Seignory of Gower, and much of the coalfield being hotly contested. The 'Holy Grail' which lay beneath Graig Trewyddfa was known as the Great Penvilia Five Foot Vein and renowned for its qualities and in great demand for the domestic market, primarily steam generating boilers and smelting furnaces.

These disputes began in the 1720s when Robert Morris, the first of the Morris family of Clasemont (the founders of Morriston) and one of the most prominent men in the early industrial history of the area, arrived on the scene. The Popkins of Fforest were foremost in the conflict with the Morris family, which lasted well into the nineteenth century. Robert Morris became involved in the industrial development of Glamorgan c.1724 through his association with Dr. John Lane of Bristol, who had leased the old Llangyfelach Copperworks at Landore, near Swansea from Thomas Popkins. In November 1726 Lane went bankrupt, and in the following year Morris entered a partnership with Richard Lockwood, Edward Gibbon and Robert Corker to take over the Llangyfelach copper works.

Problems arose almost immediately because Thomas Popkins was either unable or unwilling to fulfil his contract to supply the copper works with coal at a reduced rate; it appears that he wished to sell his coal elsewhere at a higher price. He therefore supplied the copperworks only with poor quality culm, which they could not use. When the company tried to oblige Popkins to make up the difference, disputes were inevitable.

Since a ready supply of coal for the copper works was essential, the next obvious step for Morris to take was the acquisition of at least a share in a neighbouring coalworks. In August 1728 he entered into an agreement with Kingsmill Mackworth, whose father had originally taken a lease of mines at Treboeth from the Somerset family in 1708. Kingsmill was described by Morris as 'but an indifferent collier'. Robert Morris was to pay for the sinking of a new pit and would then receive half the profits of the coalworks.

In 1729 Morris took a lease of the Lower Fforest estate which adjoined Popkins' freehold land and which the latter was also interested in, from the Duke of Beaufort. Popkins' failure to obtain the estate increased his animosity toward Morris and he refused to allow his adversary permission to build a weir, one end of which had to be tied to Popkins' land, thus frustrating plans to build a new copper works there. This was not the end of Thomas Popkins' attempts to impede the development of Morris' industrial concerns.

Price and Popkins were joined by other neighbouring coal owners in a phase of attacks on Morris' properties. During this period one of his collieries was set on fire; Mr. Popkins built a wall across a coal level and drowned it; and Mr. Price deprived another coalworks of air by blocking up air vents, resulting in the murder of six poor miners. It was during these turbulent times that the copper-smelting firm of Lockwood, Morris and Co. moved from their Llangyfelach works at Landore in 1747 to the new site at Forest (Morriston). Here they established the Forest Copperworks and production began in 1749.

By the late 1760s, three of the main antagonists were dead: Thomas Popkins died in c. 1751–52, Thomas Price in 1763 and Robert Morris in 1768. However, a legacy of bitterness and a determination to withstand any attempts, real or imagined, to extend the Duke's powers remained.

In all probability the opening of the Forest Copperworks coincided with the opening of the Clyndu Level Colliery by Lockwood Morris & Co. in 1747–48. However, in a letter sent by Gabriel Powell to the Duke of Beaufort in November 1753, he reported that John Morris had at last been fortunate to discover the 'Great Penvilia Coal Vein' at the bottom of Trewyddfa Common. The Penvilia vein was a contemporary name for the five-foot seam, which is the vein which the Clyndu Level Colliery worked, and the location given by Gabriel Powell corresponds to the location of the level.

In 1746, Robert Morris applied a lease from the Duke of Beaufort allowing him to work coal virtually anywhere on the western side of the Tawe between Landore and Morriston. He then opened up the Five Foot Penvilia Vein around Graig Trewyddfa at Clyndu Level Colliery, Morriston, partly to supply his Forest works and partly to increase his exports of coal. His collieries were not far from the sea and he wished to find a market for coals unsuitable for his furnaces. The new works was situated at the 'Highest Point of the Ordinary Tide', allowing vessels carrying copper ore to sail up the river Tawe and unload their cargoes directly at the copperworks.

Injuries and deaths were to be expected in the poor working conditions associated with early mining. In 1754 six miners were suffocated to death in the Clyndu Level; five colliers were killed at the Pentre Pit in 1776, followed by a further five in 1816; at the Weig Fach Colliery in Cwm Burlais four men met their deaths in 1873, followed by a further eighteen deaths in 1877, both accidents due to gas explosions; at the Gorse Colliery, Cwm Burlais, two men met their deaths in 1855; and Pentrefelen Colliery, near Morriston suffered a gas explosion in 1893 which left three miners dead.

Following its opening in 1843, Mynydd Newydd Colliery suffered a spate of accidents, some fatal, mainly during the time it was managed by the Swansea Coal Company:

- Dec 28 1844: Inquest on James Thomas, 36, killed at Swansea Coal Co's Mynydd Newydd Colliery.
- Jan 25 1845: Thomas Owen, William David & David Lodwick injured in explosion at Swansea Coal Company's Mynydd Newydd Colliery.

- May 22 1846: Mynydd Newydd explosion: David Jones, 14, David Jones, 12, William Lodwick, 12, & John David, 17, killed.
- Jan 01 1847: Accident on the tramroad from Mynydd Newydd Colliery to the canal near Landore.
- Nov 16 1849: William Jones, aged 15, son Thomas Jones, Caebricks, killed at Mynydd Newydd Colliery.
- Dec 12 1851: John Phillips, 20, killed at Mynydd Newydd Colliery near Swansea.
- Dec 10 1858: Explosion of fire damp at Mynydd Newydd Colliery (owned by Swansea Coal Company), some colliers sustained burns.
- May 10 1867: Inquest at Compass Public House, Caebricks, on Thomas Hughes, killed at Mynydd Newydd Colliery.
- April 02 1869: Mynydd Newydd, Llangyfelach: Joseph Mathews, 38, Thomas Mathews, 30 & Enoch Lewis 16, son of John Lewis, fireman, killed.
- Dec 10 1875: Accidental death recorded on David Williams, 42, collier, after fall at Mynydd Newydd Colliery (owned by Vivian & Son).
- Dec 26 1879: Thomas Davies, 11, of Patrick Road, Brynhyfryd, fell under wheels of tram at Mynydd Newydd Colliery tramroad.

Edward Martin, Canal Engineer and Principal Mining Surveyor to the Duke of Beaufort, had observed the best methods used for mining the rich reserves of coal in south Wales:

"The veins of coal and iron ore, in the vincinity of most of the iron works in Monmouthshire and Glamorganshire are drained and worked by levels or horizontal drifts, which opportunity is given by the deep valleys which generally run in a north and south direction, intersecting the range of coal and iron ore, which run in an east and west direction, under the high mountains, and thereby serving as main drains, so that the collier or miner here gets at the treasures of the earth, without going to the expense and labour of sinking deep pits, and erecting powerful fire-engines."

It followed that coal levels or drifts would need to be constructed with slight rising gradient inwards from the entrance allowed underground mine water to drain away from the coal face to the mine entrance and provide a trackbed for a tramway to transport the mined coal. However, deep shafts from the surface would be required to work the lower bitiminous coal seams with the erection of fire-engines.

The coal levels west of the river Tawe could reach the Great Penvilian Five Foot seam, but miners were occasionally faced with synclines (steep underground valleys) and anticlines (steep underground hills) which the coal seam would follow. However, deep shafts from the surface would be required to work the lower bituminous coal seams. Hence the Graig Trewyddfa coalfield became a mix of coal levels and pits.

In the Morriston catchment there were four pits, namely Pentrepoeth (closed 1844), Tircanol (closed 1875), Fiery Coalery (closed 1900), Water Machine Pit (closure likely on opening of Clyndu Level in 1847), Copper Pit (closed 1933) and three unidentified pits near Cwmrhydceirw (closure unknown). There were two levels: Clyndu (closed 1844), and Level y Graig (Park) (closed 1843).

In the Treboeth, Brynhyfryd and Landore catchment there were four pits: Pwll Yr Ayr (closed 1745), Cwm Pit (closed 1736), Tirdeunaw (Treboeth) Pit (closure unknown), Cwmgelly (1912), Pentre Pit (1924). There were two levels at Cwm (closed 1962) and Penvilia (closed 1924).

In the Plasmarl and Landore catchment there was one pit and a level named Plasmarl, and one pit named Landore.

At Cwmburlais, the pits comprised Worcester (closed 1898), Weigfach (year of closure unknown, Gorse (closed 1860's), Weig Fawr (closed (1898), Old Weig Fach (closed 1898), Cwm Bach (closed 1924), Gorse (closed 1860's), and Wig Fawr (closure unknown).

Cefngyfelach and Tirdonkin pits, situated near Llangyfelach, closed in 1908 and 1928 respectively.

Pentrefelen pit, situated near Morriston, and Mynydd Newydd pit, situated on Cadle common, Morriston, closed in 1893 and 1932 respectively: Mynydd Newydd Slant in Cadle closed in 1955.

However, the majority of these pits, unwittingly, had been sunk where there was a great pond of water in the basin between Landore, Morriston, Llangyfelch and Penllegaer, which extended through the workings of several connected collieries and eventually caused their demise.

The growth of the metal smelting industries in the lower Swansea Valley on the western banks of the river Tawe, also led to an increased demand for smokeless bituminous coal particularly for the copper, brass and lead smelting works situated on the west bank and a means of exporting their products. At the time collieries were linked directly to the smelting works by private tramroads which provided little flexibility for the shipping of refined copper for export or for transporting bulk coal to the refiners.

An Act of Parliament authorising the construction of the Swansea Canal was passed on 23 May 1794, and the Company were empowered to raise £60,000 by issuing shares, and a further £30,000 if required. The canal provided an economic means of transporting coal in horse drawn trains of tubs or barges to the smelting works in the lower Swansea valley and for shipping refined metals to Swansea Docks for export.

Calland's Pit was crucial to the workings of several collieries. Situated almost 450 yards east of Pentre, it was originally sunk as a coal shaft in 1762, but from 1805 it was used by John Morris II, in conjunction with the Duke of Beaufort's Landore engine, as a pumping shaft to drain all the workings on the western side of the Tawe valley

At the time of John Morris's lease of mining assets to Glasbrook and Richard in 1854, those at Callands Pumping Pit were recorded as:

"AT LANDORE PUMPING PIT Two Boilers and fittings 30 feet long by 6 feet Diameter complete. An old cylinder fit for a casing for a smaller engine. Engine House. Great. A pump pit and rods and two old capstans."

The Swansea Coal Company (See Chapter XIII) was dissolved in 1863 and most of its assets, including Callands Pit, were transferred to Vivian and Sons, owners of the Hafod Morfa Copperworks. The company continued to operate the former collieries of the Swansea Coal Co. but as coal supplies became exhausted they were closed down or sold. In 1812, Vivian and Sons sub-leased Pentre pit and Calland's pit to Pentre Collieries and Brickworks Ltd. with the requirement that they continued to pump the workings as before.

In 1896 the owners of the Pentre and Callands Pits, Landore, proposed to abandon operations resulting in the ceasing of pumping at Calland's Pit and a sectional drawing showing the levels in the pits affected as produced by mining engineer T.B. Richard in 1896.

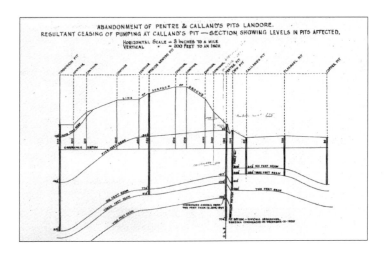

(Plate 1) Map drawn by mining engineer, T.B. Richard, 1896, showing abandonment of Pentre and Calland's Pits Landore and resultant ceasing of pumping ceasing of pumping at Calland's Pit – Section showing levels of water in pits affected. Courtesy Richard Burton Archives, Swansea University Library.

TIRDONKIN Pit worked the Four Feet Seam at a depth of 100 feet, Five Feet (Penvilian)Seam at a depth of 468 feet and the Six Feet at 775 feet.

MYNYDD NEWYDD Pit worked the Five Feet (Penvilian) Seam at a depth of 348 feet, the Six Feet Seam at a depth of 775 feet and the Three Feet at a depth of 815 feet.

PENTRE Pit worked the Five Feet (Penvilian) Seam at a depth of 50 feet, the Six Feet Seam at a depth of 417 feet, the Three Feet Seam at a depth of 475 feet and the Two Feet Seam at a depth of 595 feet. Interestingly the pit commenced sinking a borehole from the Two Feet Seam, in June 1894, to a depth of 1471 feet 10 inches, striking the Slatog, Bwdwr and Hughes's seams, in its search for new coal measures. The operation was stopped in 14 May, 1896.

TREBOETH Pit worked the Five Feet Seam at a depth of 68 feet and the Six Feet Seam at a depth of 488 feet.

PENFILIA Pit worked the Five Feet seam at a depth of 66 feet.

CWM Pit worked the Six Feet Seam at a depth of 243 feet and the Three Feet Seam at a depth of 358 feet.

CALLAND'S Pit worked the Six Feet Seam at a depth of 243 feet and the Three Feet Seam at a depth of 296 feet.

PLASMARL Pit is shown with its shaft reaching the Six Feet Seam and the Three Feet Seam, but no measurements are given.

COPPER PIT is shown with its shaft reaching the Six Feet Seam but no measurements are given.

We can safely assume that the pits shown in T.B. Richard's sectional drawing were the surviving shafts at that time ; the others having been closed largely due to the prohibitive cost of working the lower seams and the cost of pumping.

However, since all pits to the north-west of Swansea were drained by the pumping engine and sump at Calland's Pit, Landore, it came as no surprise in 1926, when pumping ceased on the grounds of cost, that the water level began to rise in all the neighbouring collieries.

In 1924 the Vivians merged with Williams Foster to form British Copper Manufacturers. In the same year Pentre pit ceased operations and the responsibility for pumping at Calland's pit reverted to Vivian and Sons. The company subsequently sold their one surviving colliery, Mynydd Newydd together with Calland's pit in 1926

The new company was unable to meet the costs of pumping at Calland's on its own and sought the assistance of other colliery owners whose mine workings were drained by Calland's. The Mynydd Newydd Colliery Company took over from Vivian and Sons in July 1926 and the owners kept on pumping for a time, but eventually ceased. As a result water levels started rise in the entire district. The pit finally closed in 1932, although the company's slant mine at Cadle continued coal production until its closure in 1965.

Indeed, at the end of the day, it was the failure of the competing mine owners to band together and fund the cost of maintaining the pumping operations at Calland's pit, that eventually led to the cessation of mining the black diamonds of the Great Penvilian Seam of Graig Trewyddfa and the eventual closure of the district's coal mines.

Finally, having examined the writers' accounts provided so far on the existence of the Clyndu Navigational Canal, coupled with our review of the Trewyddfa collieries serving the Morriston copperworks we have not uncovered any evidence to support the claim that a navigational canal was incorporated into the Clyndu Level Colliery workings. It would also appear that writers have tended to read ordnance survey maps without contours, resulting in their view of the topography of the Clyndu Level landscape becoming distorted. Moreover, the underground canal, to which writers makes reference, was undoubtedly the Graig Trewydda underground water drainage canal, which originated at Clase Bach, and fed the 'Water Machine Pit' sited close to the junction of Vicarage Road and Cwm Bath Road, providing power to a capstan shaft by means of a water-driven wheel. Also the former Clyndu Level tramway tunnel near Copper Pit station had become a drainage culvert, following the tramway's closure, and was never a lower level navigational canal. Indeed, with the absence of any tangible evidence to support writers' hunches that an underground navigational canal existed in the Clyndu Level mine, we are led to the conclusion that this means of coal transportation did not exist in the level.

The heyday of copper smelting was between 1770 and 1870, but by 1920 it was virtually over. Unfortunately for the communities around the valley, the decline and closure of works, particularly marked in the twentieth century, were not compensated by the rise of new, modern industry. The heritage and presence of dereliction and waste slag heaps, together with very restricted road access gave the impression that the former metallurgical centre of the industrial world now represented an equally large environmental pollution and planning challenge of monumental proportions because in total it represented the largest unit of such problems in south Wales, if not in Britain. The extensive closure of works in the Swansea valley after 1945 left an area of some 1,100 acres of disused buildings, works, tips, canals and railways running right into the heart of the city, which encouraged efforts to plan for reclamation and redevelopment.

In 1961, a Mr. K. J. Hilton was appointed director of an inquiry initiated by the University of Swansea, in partnershipwith the then Swansea County Council and Welsh Office, and was largely funded by the Nuffield Foundation. Mr. Hilton's team's terms of reference was "to establish the factors which inhibit the social and ecouse of land in the Lower Swansea Valley and to suggest ways in which the area should be used in the future."[1]

The terms of reference, have to a large extent, been achieved, and today the Lower Swansea Valley is a different place to when the author came to live in Morriston in the 1960's. The landscape is full of greenery, decidious trees and modern industrial buildings: the atmospheric pollution has fallen to very low levels and the prevailing winds and rainfall have helped to minimise what little there is. A typical example of this achievement can be seen at Nant Gelli at Pwll Cwm, Landore. Moreover, the copper slag tips were soon to disappear, providing a re-cycled hard core bed for the M4 motorway construction and other local building projects.

CHAPTER XVII
BIBLIOGRAPHY AND ILLUSTRATIONS

(1) 'Lower Swansea Valley Facts Sheet', M.Howell, p.8, City of Swansea, 1978.

(Plate 1) Map drawn by mining engineer, T.B. Richard, 1896, showing abandonment of Pentre and Calland's Pits Landore and resultant ceasing of pumping ceasing of pumping at Calland's Pit – Section showing levels of water in pits affected. Courtesy Richard Burton Archives, Swansea University Library. Ref: LAC/96/A21

Looking up river. 'The Forest Works near Swansea' *1792 by John 'Warwick' Smith. The Copper refining works is situated next to the canal and bridge, and on the opposite bank are the Lower Forest copper rolling and battery mill.The Beaufort bridge linked up both of Morris's works. Courtesy National Library of Wales.*

SOURCES OF ILLUSTRATIONS

Front Cover © View of the Llangyfealch Copper Works, Landore
C1716, Courtesy British Library.

Page 5 © Swansea Docks Collection.

Page 6 © O.H.M.S. 1870.

Page 13 © Swansea Docks Collection.

Page 14 © J.P.Thomas. (Author).

Page 14 © D. Hague, RCAHMW.

Page 15 © Hafod.Recalled.wordpress.com.

Page 15 © R.W. Jones.

Page 16 © COFLEIN.

Page 16 © J.P. Thomas (Author).

Page 18 © Birmingham Library Services.

Page 33 © National Portrait Gallery.

Page 35 © Courtesy British Library, Topographical Drawings.

Page 40 © Swansea Museum Ceramics Section.

Page 41 © Rhys Owain Williams.

Page 45 © National Library of Wales (Badmington Papers II).

Page 51 © J.P.Thomas (Author).

Page 52 © J.P.Thomas (Author).

Page 54 © Report of the Commission of Enquiry into the State
of Children in Employment in 1842.

Page 55 © Report of the Commission of Enquiry into the State
of Children in Employment in 1842.

Page 57 © David Johnson and Manfred Stutzer. How Mining is
Done, The Journal of Mining Collectables, Issue 46, Part II.

Page 58 © Report of the Childrens Employment Commission
(Mines) 1842.

Page 59 © Report of The Commission of Enquiry into the State
of Children in Employment 1842.

Page 62 © A. Venning, Britain's Child Slaves, Daily Mail, 17 September, 2010.

Page 63 © Report of The Commission of Enquiry into the State of Children in Employment 1842.

Page 64 © J.P. Thomas.(Author).

Page 66 © Swansea Reference Library.

Page 68 © Swansea University Library, Richard Burton Archives.

Page 69 © Bristol Museum.

Page 69 © O.H.M.S. 1890–1920.

Page 74 © National Library of Scotland.

Page 76 © J.P. Thomas. (Author).

Page 77 © West Glamorgan Archives (Badmington Collection Vol.72).

Page 78 © West Glamorgan Archives (Badmington Collection Vol.72).

Page 79 © Joyce.H.M. Banks, A Nineteenth Century Colliery Railway 1974.

Page 80 © P.R. Reynolds. South West Wales Industrial Archaeology Society.

Page 81 © J.P. Thomas. (Author).

Page 82 © J.P. Thomas. (Author).

Page 83 © J.P. Thomas. (Author).

Page 83 © J.P. Thomas. (Author).

Page 84 © J.P. Thomas. (Author).

Page 85 © National Library of Scotland.

Page 87 © J.P. Thomas. (Author).

Page 89 © O.H.M.S. 1870.

Page 90 © Welsh Papers on Line 21 April 1909.

Page 90 © J.P. Thomas. (Author).

Page 91 © Lizzie East.

Page 91 © J.P. Thomas, (Author).

Page 95 © Clyndu Water Machine Pit – Nat. Library Scotland

Page 96 © Researchgate net.

Page 97 © University of Swansea, Richard Burton Archives.

Page 98 © J.P. Thomas. (Author).

Page 98 © J.P. Thomas. (Author).

Page 100 © National Library of Scotland.

Page 102 © National Library of Wales.

Page 103 © Lanrashire Industrial History Society.

Page 103 © O.H.M.S.

Page 104 © J.P. Thomas. (Author).

Page 104 © J.P. Thomas. (Author).

Page 104 © J.P. Thomas. (Author).

Page 105 © Trevithick Society.

Page 106 © J.P. Thomas. (Author).

Page 106 © J.P. Thomas. (Author).

Page 107 © Morriston History Forum.

Page 107 © Morriston History Forum.

Page 109 © SLS Coastal Surveys 2014.

Page 110 © SLS Coastal Surveys 2014.

Page 110 © SLS Coastal Surveys 2014.

Page 112 © The Open Mechanical Engineering Journal 2018.

Page 112 © Nevis Books Website.

Page 113 © Navis Books Website.

Page 114 © J.P. Thomas.(Author).

Page 114 © Scolt's Pit Engine House & Mining Remains.

Page 118 © National Library of Scotland.

Page 119 © O.H.M.S. 1879.

Page 119 © National Library of Scotland.

Page 120 © O.H.M.S. 1876.

Page 121 © O.H.M.S. 1870.

Page 123 © O.H.M.S. 1879.

Page 124 © Morriston History Society.

Page 125 © J.P. Thomas. (Author).

Page 125 © J.P. Thomas. (Author).

Page 126 © National Library of Scotland.

Page 127 © Men & Women of South Wales & Monmouthshire, Western Mail, 1897.

Page 128 © M. Fretwell.

Page 128 © J.P. Thomas. (Author).

Page 129 © South Wales Evening Post, 1 May 1930.

Page 132 © O.H.M.S. 1876.

Page 133 © O.H.M.S. 1876.

Page 134 © West Glamorgan Archives.

Page 135 © J.P. Thomas. (Author).

Page 135 © J.P. Thomas. (Author).

Page 136 © O.H.M.S. 1876.

Page 137 © West Glamorgan County Council Engineers Department, 1999.

Page 137 © Swansea Docks Collection.

Page 138 © Welsh Coal Mines Forum.

Page 138 © O.H.M.S. 1870.

Page 139 © British Transport Board.

Page 149 © John Hutchings.

Page 150 © Swansea Museum Collection.

Page 152 © Swansea Docks Collection.

Page 154 © Badmington Collection Group II 1454 National
Library of Wales. See also S.R. Hughes, Collieries in Wales.
Engineering and Architecture, RCAHW, 1994.

Page 155 © Badmington Collection Group II 1454 National
Library of Wales See also S.R. Hughes, Collieries in Wales.
Engineering and Architecture, RCAHW, 1994.

Page 156 © Badmington Collection Group II 1282 & 1283
National Library of Wales. See also S.R. Hughes, Collieries
in Wales. Engineering and Architecture, RCAHW, 1994.

Page 157 © National Library of Wales.

Page 158 © O.H.M.S. 189–1920.

Page 159 © Swansea Museum Collection.

Page 160 © O.H.M.S. 1876,

Page 167 © Birmingham Reference Library, Boulton & Watt
Collection,

Page 169 © J.P.Thomas. (Author).

Page 170 © J.P.Thomas. (Author).

Page 171 © O.H.M.S. 1879.

Page 171 © Swansea Library & Information Services Archives.

Page 172 © O.H.M.S. 1879.

Page 172 © J.P. Thomas. (Author).

Page 173 © O.H.M.S. 1879.

Page 173 © O.H.M.S. 1979.

Page 174 © F.Cowley.

Page 175 © Treboeth Historical & Pictorial Record.Treboeth Historical Society.

Page 175 © J.P. Thomas. (Author).

Page 176 © Treboeth Historical & Pictorial Record.Treboeth Historical Society.

Page 176 © J.P. Thomas. (Author).

Page 181 © Aerofilms.

Page 183 © Treboeth Historical & Pictorial Record.Treboeth Historical Society.

Page 184 © Treboeth Historical & Pictorial Record.Treboeth Historical Society.

Page 187 © O.H.M.S. 1879.

Page 191 © West Glamorgan Archives.

Page 192 © Swansea Reference Library. Swansea History Project 4.

Page 194 © O.H.M.S. 1879.

Page 195 © O.H.M.S. 1879.

Page 197 © O.H.M.S. 1879.

Page 200 © O.H.M.S. 1879.

Page 202 © O.H.M.S. 1879.

Page 204 © O.H.M.S. 1914.

Page 210 © George Grant Francis, The Smelting of Copper in the Swansea District from the time of Elizabeth to the present day. London, 1881.

Page 211 © Wales on Line co.uk.

Page 212 © John Ball.

Page 213 © J.P. Thomas. (Author).

Page 214 © J.P. Thomas. (Author).

Page 214 © J.P. Thomas. (Author).

Page 215 © J.P. Thomas. (Author).

Page 216 © COFLEIN.

Page 216 © O.H.M.S. 1881.

Page 218 © 'Wales on Line' October 2014.

Page 219 © West Glamorgan Archives.

Page 219 © West Glamorgan Archives.

Page 220 © West Glamorgan Archives.

Page 220 © West Glamorgan Archives.

Page 221 © West Glamorgan Archives.

Page 221 © West Glamorgan Archives.

Page 225 © National Museum of Wales Collections.

Page 226 © HMS Victory Museum, Portsmouth.

Page 226 © City and County of Swansea, Swansea Museum Collection.

Page 229 © City and County of Swansea. Swansea Museum Collection.

Page 236 © Bowes Railway.

Page 236 © Geoff Wright. Uphill and Downhill: Inclined Planes.

Page 237 © Bowes Railway.

Page 238 © O.H.M.S. 1890.

Page 239 © J.P. Thomas. (Author).

Page 240 © O.H.M.S. 188.

Page 242 © Welsh Coal Mines Forums.

Page 243 © O.H.M.S. 1889.

Page 244 © O.H.M.S. 1873.

Page 245 © O.H.M.S. 1876.

Page 245 © J.P. Thomas. (Author).

Page 246 © O.H.M.S. 1890.

Page 247 © Aerofilms.

Page 250 © City and County of Swansea. Swansea Museum Collection.

Page 250 © Royal Air Force 1946. RCAHMW.

Page 251 © O.H.M.S. 1881.

Page 251 © Royal Institution of South Wales.

Page 252 © J.P. Thomas. (Author).

Page 252 © London Gazette 8 August, 1932 .

Page 253 © O.H.M.S. 1937.

Page 254 © O.H.M.S. 1880.

Page 255 © O.H.M.S. 1879.

Page 255 © National Library of Scotland.

Page 256 © O.H.M.S. 1869.

Page 257 © J.P.Thomas. (Author).

FÜR AUTOREN A HEART FOR AUTHORS À L'ÉCOUTE DES AUTEURS MIA ΚΑΡΔΙΑ ΓΙΑ ΣΥΓ
FÖR FÖRFATTARE UN CORAZÓN POR LOS AUTORES YAZARLARIMIZA GÖNÜL VERELIM S
PER AUTORI ET HJERTE FOR FORFATTERE EEN HART VOOR SCHRIJVERS TEMOS OS AU
ZÖINKÉRT SERCE DLA AUTORÓW EIN HERZ FÜR AUTOREN A HEART FOR AUTHORS À L'ÉCO
AÇÃO ВСЕЙ ДУШОЙ К АВТОРАМ ETT HJÄRTA FÖR FÖRFATTARE À LA ESCUCHA DE LOS AU
ΓΙΑ ΣΥΓΓΡΑΦΕΙΣ UN CUORE PER AUTORI ET HJERTE FOR FORFATTERE EE
ZÖINKÉRT SERCE DLA AUTORÓW EIN HERZ F
ACÃO ВСЕЙ ДУШОЙ К АВТОРАМ ETT HJÄRTA F

The author

John 'Peter' Thomas moved to Morriston, the cradle of Britain's copper smelting industry, in the 1960s. He was struck by the vast lunar landscape of copper slag heaps and derelict metal smelting works on the valley floor, the whole area devoid of vegetation due to the ground having been contaminated by copper smelting waste slag and former acid rain emissions.

He attended Dynevor Grammar School, Swansea, Swansea College of Technology, and later the universities of Birmingham and Wales, where he graduated. He served an engineering apprenticeship followed by several years experience in manufacturing and engineering and the local mining industry at the now closed Brynlliw Colliery, Grovesend. He is now employed as a lecturer in Engineering and Design at Gower College, Gorseinon.

The publisher

He who stops getting better stops being good.

This is the motto of novum publishing, and our focus is on finding new manuscripts, publishing them and offering long-term support to the authors.
Our publishing house was founded in 1997, and since then it has become THE expert for new authors and has won numerous awards.

Our editorial team will peruse each manuscript within a few weeks free of charge and without obligation.

You will find more information about novum publishing and our books on the internet:

www.novum-publishing.co.uk

John Peter Thomas

The Rise and Fall of the Penclawdd Canal and Railway or Tramroad Company 1811–1865

ISBN 978-3-99064-082-1
282 pages

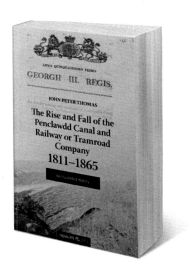

Anyone wanting to learn more about this fascinating local history must read this book. Brimming with important historical communications and insightful information, it should be a feature in homes of those who either live or have ties with the area.